EXPEDITIONS
The Experts' Way

other books by John Blashford-Snell

WHERE THE TRAILS RUN OUT (1974)
IN THE STEPS OF STANLEY (1975)

EXPEDITIONS
The Experts' Way

edited by John Blashford-Snell
and Alistair Ballantine

FABER AND FABER LIMITED
3 Queen Square London

First published in 1977
by Faber and Faber Limited
3 Queen Square London WC1
Printed in Great Britain by
BAS Printers Limited
Wallop, Hampshire

British Library Cataloguing in Publication Data

Expeditions.
1. Expeditions, Scientific
I. Blashford-Snell, John Nicholas
II. Ballantine, Alistair
910'.4 Q115

ISBN 0-571-11021-5
ISBN 0-571-11116-5 Pbk

CONTENTS

ILLUSTRATIONS

ACKNOWLEDGEMENTS

The editors would like to thank the following for the use of photographs: John Cleare, for plates 2 and 3; Paul Arengo-Jones, for plate 4; Roy Warden, for plate 5; John Turner, for plate 6; Wendy Hinds, for plate 12; William Austin, for plates 15 and 16; and Kelvin Kent for plates 17, 18 and 19. Our thanks are also due to Michael Saunders for the diagram of the Land-Rover on page 106; Keith Morgan-Jones for the cartoons; and to Neil Hyslop for the illustrations in Chapter 8. We would also like to thank Christopher Hawkesworth for supplying the information for the section on canoes and kayaks in Chapter 8.

INTRODUCTION

The world of expeditioning has no hierarchy, no rank and few prizes. Most explorers are individualists and not all of them are authors, in fact some positively shun publicity. So to try and gather a body of experts together to write of their activities has itself been something of a challenge. However we are extremely grateful to our authors who have given us the benefit of their specialist knowledge and experience. Not only does each chapter deal with a different field of 'expeditioning', but each demands a different approach. Thus the chapters are very dissimilar in style. However, although each chapter is an entity in itself, the whole work provides a unique manual for all members and organizers of expeditions, not least on the vitally important aspect of selection of team members. On an expedition everyone is important, for if it is to be successful its members must form a powerful team but, like a chain, any team is as strong as its weakest link.

To write a general book about every type of expedition is not easy and when we were asked to do just that, we had to consider carefully what particular activities should be included. We decided to select the main types of expedition and have tried to describe these with both practical and theoretical examples. Of course, in a book of this size we cannot hope to produce a comprehensive work and we see it simply as an introduction to adventure and modern scientific exploration.

JOHN BLASHFORD-SNELL
ALISTAIR BALLANTINE

London 1976

1. EXPEDITION PLANNING AND LOGISTICS

by Kelvin Kent

> 'Next I would place sound, thorough, meticulously detailed planning. On Everest the problems of organisation assume the proportions of a military campaign.' LORD HUNT, *Leader 1953 Everest Expedition*

This chapter is largely the result of spontaneous but accumulated ideas arising from my own participation and leadership of previous expeditions. It is by no means complete or definitive but it does aim to bring out points of planning and logistics common to most types of expedition.

In order to simplify and not overlap I have subdivided the chapter into various headings. These are:

Concept and pre-planning
Sponsorship, public relations and finance
Selection of expedition members
Documentation
Movements, transportation and supply
Photography—before and after

I believe that some essential factors exist which bind everything together and they are: firstly, the paramount need for a good reconnaissance or if that is not possible the search for accurate and up-to-date information on such matters as local government, our own embassy or consulate, a basic idea of the lines of communication involved, the likely area for the Base Camp, availability and accessibility of local transport facilities, knowledge of local food supplies, the nature of communications to be employed and whether they are permitted by the Government, medical facilities and liaison with local institutions and scientific bodies. Secondly, a good appreciation of the fact that any expedition abroad is at the invitation of the country concerned and that we, the foreigners, are subject to their laws and dependent upon their hospitality. Thus a knowledge and understanding of languages, customs, religion, politics and the people is most important. Only by knowing what is involved can appropriate respect be paid.

The successful expedition starts its planning early and allows for delays, inflation, frustration and bureaucracy. It takes into account things like the need for a balance between scientific fieldwork and the exploratory aim. It is also aware of the effect of attrition in the second half of a medium or long duration expedition. This factor alone is extremely important. It means in practice that after about six weeks of a really tough expedition most people start to run down. However good the rations are, people tend to get weaker and this often coincides with a lengthening line of communication and a need for more people to man it. Thus any hold-up of progress through poor administration and logistics can make attrition worse still and seriously prolong the expedition. It is this phase where accidents can occur most easily. On the other hand a quick rapier-like thrust or Alpine push may get into serious difficulty if the objective is not reached and supplies run out or cannot keep up. If bad weather conditions then set in, all ingredients for a disaster are present. A leader has to maintain a balance but he must be prepared to use either method when the situation dictates and maintain the flexibility necessary to achieve this.

Good planning, administration and logistics are essential functions and are integral to success. Planning itself appears obvious but is not always estimated in perspective. Logistics cover the fields of movement, transport, re-supply and replenishment, casualty evacuation, rations and cooking, dumping of supplies and forward supply teams, installation of the rear party and base camp, handling of materials, maintenance, recovery, refuelling, repairs and administration. Any expedition from four to a thousand men will have to take all of these things into account and adapt them to the situation, ground and time. The key and overriding factor which enables the system to work is communications.

CONCEPT AND PRE-PLANNING

Aims

It does not really matter what the stated aim of an expedition is so long as it is right for that particular expedition. Above all it should be concise and not woolly and it must say exactly what the expedition is setting out to accomplish. For example 'To climb Kangchenjunga' or 'To navigate the Tana River from its source to the Indian Ocean carrying out a scientific study of the riverine forests en route'.

Many expeditions these days tend to arrange a trip to a country they want to see, like Nepal or Peru, and then invent some sort of admissible aim under the guise of biology or ecology. The end result, which is not likely to fool many people or gain large financial support, can result in something like: '. . . Nepal expedition to gain some understanding of the ecology of the natural montane tundra ecosystems developed in a sub-tropical latitude'. I wonder?

Research in the early stages always pays off. It may be that exactly what is being planned has been done before or, worse still, is planned by two or three other expeditions for the same time. This does not mean that the plan should be abandoned but it does follow that expeditions might be able to get together to plan on a coordinated basis and follow up the research and aims of previous expeditions. There is often a great need to verify knowledge and to check on movements, growth, ecology and measurements recorded at an earlier time. A good example of this is found in the Young Explorers' Trust Iceland Unit's expeditions for glaciological research in Iceland.

Maps

Parallel with this type of basic research should be the procurement of good maps. A large atlas is not sufficient and detailed up-to-date maps of particular areas can be hard to come by. The main commercial supply centre of maps in Great Britain is Edward Stanford Ltd. 12–14 Long Acre, London WC2E 9LP. They have a large stock and are most helpful. Tourist offices or Embassies of the countries concerned can usually offer assistance as well.

Ideally the requirement is for a combination of maps:

1. Ordinary commercial road maps, normally obtainable locally or, in the case of Europe and USA, at Stanfords and on the spot petrol stations. The AA and RAC are good for Europe and transit to the Far East, and Michelin cover North Africa.
2. Large-scale maps of at least 1:500,000.
3. Small-scale maps of say 1:125,000 or 1:50,000.

If there is still any difficulty it is worth writing to the Directorate of Military Survey who can sell maps if they hold them in sufficient quantity. Failing that, they may be able to give the name of an agency who specializes in that area.

The Royal Geographical Society, 1 Kensington Gore, London SW7 2AR (Tel 01-589 5466) may also be able to assist.

Recently a new science has emerged called photogeology and remote sensing. This involves aerial and in particular, satellite photography. The pictures obtained can be used to produce maps at scales between 1:1 million to 1:200,000 and in some cases even better. Often the satellite photographs themselves are far superior to any available maps and there is no doubt that this form of imagery will become more and more useful to expeditions (see pp. 85–6).

One last point about maps is fairly obvious but often ignored. Maps are vital in the areas of operation and their protection is most important. Map holders (cardboard tubes) should be taken to carry bulk supplies, and plastic map covers, fablon or waterproof polyurethane spray can be used to waterproof maps and stop them from cracking and fraying.

Exactly how to use a map and techniques of map reading and navigation, especially in jungle, cannot be explained here but one thing is certain: it is not much use taking maps of remote areas, if the people who are to operate there cannot interpret them or use them in those particular conditions and geography. Before leaving make sure that all members of the team are competent map readers.

Line of communication

Having decided firmly on an aim and obtained maps for planning, in addition to getting details of local ports, airports, towns, contacts, new roads, availability of local transport and facilities, etc., the next logical step is to plan a line of communication. In effect, this is a supply and communication line from the firm base, which may well be where the main facilities are, to the area of operation. This is often not easy and may well require a reconnaissance trip beforehand. In the case of, say, climbing a mountain in the Himalayas or conducting a scientific survey in a specific place, the area of operation is fixed and the line of communication can be set up and maintained. The only consideration to be taken into account is the weather. For example, in the monsoon it may not be possible to use airstrips or certain roads. These may become usable later when the monsoon is finished and therefore two methods of communication, possibly over the same route, have to be considered.

In other types of expedition which involve a journey of exploration, the line of communication (L of C) is very much more difficult and more complex. It may be, as in the Darien Gap Expedition (1971–2), that the journey traverses more than one country or, as in the case of the Zaïre River Expedition (1974–5), that the distances are so vast as to make supply from one end impossible after, say, the half-way mark.

First of all, what has the L of C got to do? It serves a number of functions and these are simply:

1. Supply of local and fresh rations.
2. Supply of urgently required items from a main facility location e.g. local cash currency, repaired items, spare parts.
3. Supply of mail.
4. Provision of opportunity for visits (possibly by local officials or joining scientists/members).
5. Casualty evacuation.
6. Scientific sample evacuation.
7. Mail, film, report outlet.

Note that half of these functions are 'both way' features. This may seem obvious but as a party goes forward into unknown territory it becomes more and more difficult to achieve. It may be, for instance, that a helicopter or light aircraft can airdrop vital supplies and mail to a partly hidden camp beneath the jungle canopy below, but how are they going to get out samples, mail and an injured man?

There is no mathematical solution: the best possible use must be made of the geography and the facilities available. This may include, as it does in Himalayan expeditions, the fixing up with local 'contractors' further down the trail, for the supply of fresh rations, firewood, paraffin and so on as well as the hiring of a number of mail runners, who run in relays from the base of the mountain to the nearest airstrip and/or radio station which may be five days away. They then come back carrying incoming items to complete the cycle.

Intermediate positions on the L of C

In the jungle areas it may become necessary actually to cut out a helicopter landing site or go to work with local people on rejuvenating an old missionary airstrip that could be used again by a light aircraft.

Another method usually adopted is to leapfrog a series of forward supply teams, ideally along the proposed route, or where this is not possible, to establish a lateral supply base to one side of the main route which is accessible by air and possibly by sea. The latter is obviously impossible in landlocked countries but it could be that a site is found where supplies, etc., can be flown in and then transferred to river craft, using waterways to reach the main route. These 'intersection points' can be preplanned and utilized to great benefit, both ways.

Sometimes a Scientific Party may wish to conduct research off of the main route. This also has to be considered, especially as the amount of equipment may be proportionately much heavier than other sections of the expedition. Indeed, when this becomes the case the whole idea of the original aim must be carefully considered. In some instances if the weight or balance is not right, neither the scientific programme nor the exploratory aim will be achieved because the logistics and extra burden on L of C planning will not be able to keep up.

Radio

An additional factor in L of C planning is radio communications. For anything more than communicating over very short distances with virtual line of sight characteristics, high frequency transceivers are required. VHF (walkie talkies) are only suitable for between one and five miles maximum and certainly no use in jungle. They are of course ideal for small groups working separately on, say, the same glacier or from a forward base to a working party up the same valley. Clearances for frequencies or crystals are usually simple but normally have to go through the local GPO or Telecommunications Ministry.

HF (high frequency) clearances are more difficult and not always given. On the other hand, some countries demand their

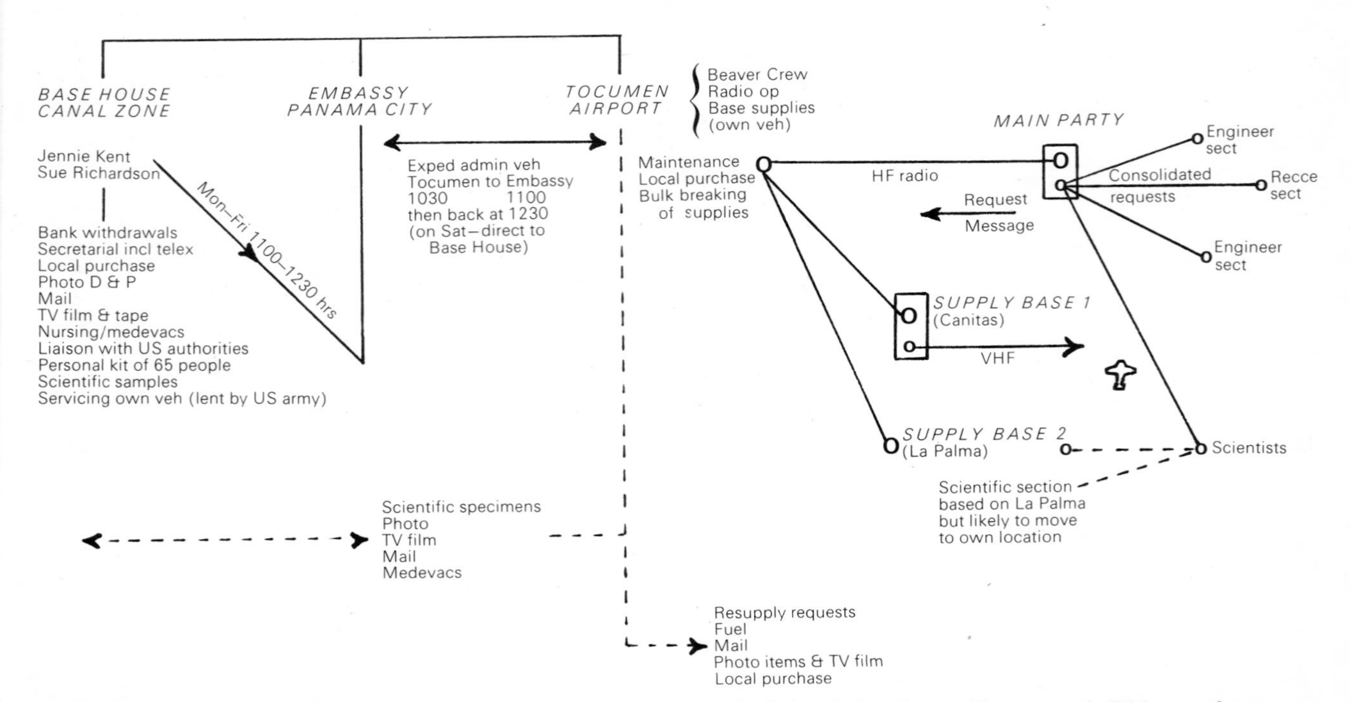

Where a line of communication is established it is essential for everyone to know how it functions and how to use it. This sort of diagram gets amended as the expedition progresses.

inclusion on grounds of safety. In these cases certain frequencies have to be predetermined to be compatible with local agencies.

When considering HF, which covers frequencies from approximately 2 to 30 Megahertz, it is usual to think of sky wave propagation using a wire or copper braided antenna which is slung between two masts or thrown up into trees. The centre point of this antenna converges into a coaxial 'feeder' or lead which runs from the high slung wire to the set. In jungle, the actual line which the wire follows has often to be physically cut out as a path between the foliage and the angle of this wire depends on directions of base station and other factors.

HF sets need far more power than smaller VHF sets and are correspondingly heavier. They may need a charging engine and will certainly need an experienced operator. If rechargeable (nickel cadmium) batteries are taken, it may necessitate an arrangement whereby a pool of batteries is included and periodically extricated from radio stations for recharging centrally. In their place, recharged batteries are airdropped or supplied. Ideally, however, the answer is to use a modification or accessory which allows the radio to operate from ordinary and easily obtainable torch batteries (U2s).

Distances to be worked cannot be laid down but there is no reason why ranges of up to 1,000 miles cannot be obtained on voice using a set weighing about eighteen pounds. Ironically it is usually the shorter distances which are most difficult like 15–30 miles and it should be borne in mind that interference is greater in the tropics than in other latitudes and that HF is unlikely to be of much use between 1600 hrs and 0600 hrs. (VHF is not affected by night-time interference.)

In many large expeditions communications are vital. On Everest each camp up the mountain is a day away from the next one and thus Camp 6 is nearly a physical week from Base. Base itself is three weeks walk from Kathmandu.

In the Darien, radio communications were used to link various sections of the expedition over nearly 300 miles

DARIEN GAP CROSSING-COMMUNICATIONS DIAGRAM

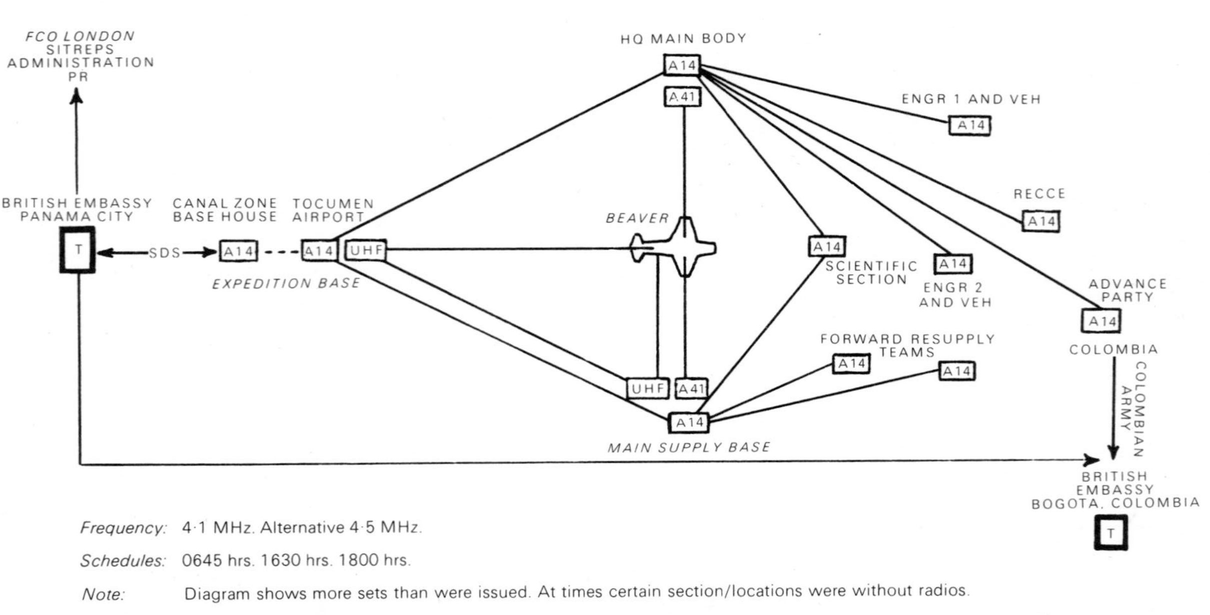

Frequency: 4·1 MHz. Alternative 4·5 MHz.

Schedules: 0645 hrs. 1630 hrs. 1800 hrs.

Note: Diagram shows more sets than were issued. At times certain section/locations were without radios.

On the Darien Gap Expedition the various elements were strung out over 300 miles in two countries, with nothing but jungle and swamp in between. The expedition depended entirely on air and river resupply and this could not have been achieved without HF radio communications. Backing this up as rear links to UK and lateral comms between the two British Embassies at Panama and Bogota was diplomatic telex, which was both quick and efficient and also saved a fortune in civil post office charges.

traversing Panama and Colombia. The Beaver aircraft which dropped supplies used radio to speak to ground parties which could not be seen from the air. In Zaïre, the problems and distances were even larger. Indeed, without this type of communication it is unlikely that a major expedition could be mounted and be successful in the time scale available.

Where to get hold of radios is a much-asked question. The answer is that it is easy enough if the expedition proposes to buy them but not so easy if the expedition merely wishes to borrow them. Sometimes a compromise can be reached by hiring them from a manufacturing firm and in all cases a prerequisite will be the onus of responsibility for insurance. The ideal solution involves participation by the Army and use of their sets, but this is not always possible. The alternative solution rests with goodwill of certain firms who try to help but who are inundated with requests.

Some examples of L of C and Radio Communication diagrams are included in this section as an indication of the scale involved. In one such diagram it will be seen that the Initial Deployment Chain is shown. This is designed to enable the system to be worked efficiently and to establish the method by which administration on a major expedition is set up.

Conclusion

A good expedition must have a reasonable idea of how it is going to function on the ground before the arrival of the main party. This normally involves considerable investigation and preparatory work and nearly always relies upon the expertise and initiative of a high-grade advance party who can set it up and liaise at the right level. It becomes the local foundation upon which the expedition is built.

SPONSORSHIP, PUBLIC RELATIONS AND FINANCE

Letterhead

The days of amateurs chipping in a few thousand pounds each to finance an expedition have long since gone. The cost of mounting expeditions has risen. The need for raising funds is therefore greater at a time when economically the situation is worse.

There is no real escape from the cost of an expedition. It is always higher than budgeted and if too great a sum is shown for inflation and contingencies in the estimated expenses, the result is likely to put off would-be helpers. There is therefore an ever growing need for good presentation, slick public relations and the knowledge and confidence needed to sell an expedition before it leaves this country. Even a Ministry of Defence expedition has to raise considerable funds and although considered 'official', is not actually sponsored. It is really encouraged and supported in kind with perhaps a grant from Adventurous Training funds.

All large expeditions should start by producing their own letterheaded paper. A crisp eye-catching design or motif often helps and it is not uncommon to call in the services of a professional designer. The letterhead must obviously give the name of the expedition, contact address of the leader or secretary and, if possible, patrons and sponsors. At the bottom the names of expedition Committee Members can also be given, if appropriate, and mention should be made of where cheques can be sent and to whom payable.

It is important to understand what is meant by these terms because if wrongly used much harm can be done. A patron is normally someone well-known and respected who allows their name to be used in conjunction with the expedition by means of passive support and interest. Patrons have to be approached and asked. They usually require to know a lot about the proposed venture before they will lend their name to it. The importance of the patron is normally related to the size and importance of the task undertaken by the expedition.

Sponsors

Sponsors are companies or institutions which actively support the expedition financially or materially in the same way as they do car racing or golf championships. The fact that a firm generously offers a quantity of free produce does not necessarily make it a sponsor. Equally, a museum or university which perhaps offers to send a scientist or liaises on the collection of specimens is not a sponsor, even though it may give funds to offset costs. Care must therefore be taken not to show a helper or a learned body as a sponsor unless they specifically agree and provide funds. Examples of recent sponsors are Barclays Bank, who sponsored the 1975 Everest Expedition; Whitbreads, who have sponsored the Round the World Yacht Race; and the National Geographical Society, who have sponsored several big expeditions. Other institutions such as the Royal Geographical Society, Mount Everest Foundation, British Mountaineering Council, National Sports Council, Winston Churchill Memorial Trust, Dulverton Trust, Frederick Soddy Trust, Gilchrist Educational Trust, Godman Fund, local education authorities and others have been most helpful in the past with grants and/or loans to expeditions. Again these do not necessarily make them sponsors, although one idea exists whereby an institution or firm agrees to underwrite an expedition's costs on the basis that any profits made at the end are ploughed back into the institution concerned. This is a sort of sponsorship with strings.

In most cases what is obtained is support and assistance. It is therefore best to list these people or bodies as supporters and not sponsors.

Another method of funding now receiving consideration is the concept of a limited company whereby the members themselves raise money to cover the costs in the hope that at the end they will at least break even or possibly make a small profit.

Committees

An expedition committee is often set up at the beginning to add status and respectability as well as being useful to the expedition itself and helpful in overseeing the raising of funds and pre-expedition decision making. Such a committee can often be of great advantage during the expedition itself when help may be needed and it is certainly useful at the end when matters are tied up. The obvious disadvantage with a committee is that it can cramp the leader's style and occasionally lead to exasperating situations involving key decision-making in the middle of a crucial phase of an expedition. Nevertheless the basic idea of a committee is sound and often a committee of respected people is a necessary function of fund raising or sponsorship.

The prospectus

Of course no impressive letterhead is going to be of much use without a well thought-out and easy-to-read synopsis of the expedition's general outline or plan and dates. This again is worth having done professionally and in the case of very large expeditions, several thousand copies might be needed. It should have pictures and maps, show the aim clearly and emphasize the difficulties and challenges involved, together with the benefits to be derived. It should show the names and qualifications of the members and list the proposed budget. If possible (and here we come to the chicken and egg position) it should include helpers, museum and university links and any scientific research to be carried out. Above all it should be well produced, discriminating in content and actually emphasize what appeal is to be made for help and funds and where cheques should be sent. It must also offer to acknowledge any assistance given.

To be of use, this sort of thing has to be produced the year before the expedition sets out. A last-minute prospectus will not attract attention and, in any case, most firms who are in a position to assist have themselves to plan their donations and contributions on a set scale within their own financial year's budget or through the Charities Commission at certain set times of the year.

A helpful book on the subject—the *Directory of Grant Making Trusts*—is published regularly by the Charities Aid fund of the National Council of Social Services, 26 Bedford Square, London WC1B 3HH. This and the Educational Charities whose address is 3 Endsleigh Street, London WC1H 0DS are sometimes worth referring to and following up.

Public relations

Public relations at this stage in an expedition's planning may be handled by the leader, by the committee or even by the sponsor (if there is one) or independently by an agent. Together with fund raising, the two functions are closely tied up and interdependent. Quite simply, PR's function is to publicize the expedition in such a way that it will gain the support and interest of the maximum number of people. Even if one sponsor pays for the whole thing, he will want a return for his investment. Other helpers and firms will also want to gain maximum PR exposure for their particular company or product.

The best and nowadays most accepted method of media support involves the arrangement of contracts with television companies, newspapers, magazines and book publishers. The whole thing is fiercely competitive and large expeditions with good previous reputations often put this work into the hands of a literary agent who knows the form and can negotiate for the best deals. The whole subject is complex and may involve syndication rights, photographic and written copyright, broadcasting restrictions and control of film and pictures. If the object is to raise a large sum of money (for example £120,000 for a major Himalayan expedition), then this is the answer. It also pays off when would-be manufacturers, suppliers and helpers know that their product or name will receive TV, book or newspaper coverage. This, in turn, encourages them to help as they realize that the venture is being taken seriously by the media.

It will by now be seen that a modern expedition of any size is a considerable commercial undertaking and much of this work falls on to the shoulders of the leader (see also under *Lectures*, page 26).

Finances

Having discussed fund raising it is appropriate to include a summary of the type of finances involved. In my experience the biggest single expenditure is travel, especially if airfreight is involved. (The 1972 Everest Expedition's airfare and freight bill was £20,000.) The next highest expenditure is usually food and this is accentuated if fuel and firewood are not plentiful in the area. A guide for headings of expenditure might be:

1. Administration
Secretarial, Postage, Printing, Publicity and Advertising.

2. Equipment
Vehicles, Clothing, Scientific, Medical and Specialist.

3. Insurance

4. Shipping or airtravel
Fares, Freight and Re-exporting costs of non consumable items and samples/specimens.

5. Food
Prepacked, Local fresh rations and Fuel.

6. Subsistence and maintenance costs in the field

7. Local labour, guides, porters, liaison officers

8. Porterage and local transportation

9. Fuel for aircraft, vehicles, outboard motors, generators, cookers

10. Radio communications including batteries

11. Sundries

12. Professional charges

13. Bank interest

14. Post-expedition expenses
(including the Final Report and pictures/articles for contributing firms)

15. Contingencies
(say 10%)

Of course each expedition is different and item 6, for example, can be very large indeed if it includes accommodation at the port of entry and departure, mail runners, local labour, customs duty, local purchases, repairs, local secretarial expenses, bonuses, royalties (for permission to climb a mountain or penetrate certain areas) and so on.

INCOME

On the income side much depends on the PR expertise and unflinching confidence of the leader and his administratively minded members. But whatever is worked out, fund raising income is derived from three sources; the media, industry and the public. Combining all three, a possible list of recoveries could be made from:

1. Book royalties, 2. TV Company, 3. Newspaper, 4. Sale of posters and postcards, 5. Sale of philatelic covers, 6. Advertising and donations, 7. Major sponsors and helpers (cash or kind), 8. Possible sale of kit and equipment at the end of the expedition to local people or incoming expedition, 9. Post-expedition presentations, 10. Lectures, 11. Sale of articles, pictures etc.

LECTURES

It follows that the more interest that can be generated before and during the expedition, the greater will be the demand for lectures and articles afterwards. The lecture programme itself can bring in several thousand pounds if projected at the right level and well organized. Naturally it may be necessary to appoint someone outside the expedition who will arrange lectures or, better still, to arrange area lectures with two or three speakers in large halls through an intermediary who earns for himself a percentage of the income for the evening. The lecturers can collect expenses and the balance goes to expedition funds.

CONTRACTS AND CONTROL

Normally an expedition's literary agent or sensible leader will obtain signatures from all members relating to the contract they undertake to fulfil on lecturing, use of pictures and articles. There may be a set period of, say, twelve months after which members are free to lecture and produce written material free-lance.

To make the lecturing programme and other commitments effective it is usual for all pictures to end up at a central agency and for a lecture set to be copied for each member who could purchase their own set out of their own money. Similarly some good originals may have to be earmarked for the book, magazines or sponsors. Others may have to be copied for helping manufacturers or firms (of which there may be up to two hundred).

Prior to the expedition leaving and during the expedition itself the PR or literary agent, possibly in conjunction with the Committee, may put out press releases which would be picked up by national and local press. This would stimulate interest.

RELEASES

In the country in which the expedition is taking place PR is more difficult. It may well be that the country demands that all releases concerning an expedition are made first from its own foreign ministry; or it may be that contracts with a TV or newspaper company here demand they receive exclusive coverage. The handling of this type of situation is a specialized art and sometimes involves the intentional 'leak' to pacify local stringers and journalists who feel they have a right to keep their own country informed and who also get paid for 'outage' from the press agencies they represent.

Bad handling of PR can do immeasurable damage and the situation has to be played very carefully, especially when parallel methods of reporting are used. In Nepal, for example, all news of camps reached and summit successes or tragedies has to be passed to the Ministry of Foreign Affairs for release by them to their own local press and agencies. It is well to respect these conditions.

OBLIGATIONS

Perhaps the most important point of all concerns the honouring of obligations made in the fund raising stage. The importance of this cannot be over stressed. It is all too easy when a tired expedition returns for it to fragment and go its various ways. The burden of administrative tasks at the end is very great indeed and it is only fair that every person who helped is thanked with appropriate reports, pictures and personal letters.

Very seldom is an expedition solvent when it returns. Sometimes it can take up to five years to clear a deficit and often the whole workload is left to one or two people. The best way to clear the account is by lecturing vigorously and appealing for further donations or grants. Everyone should join in this responsibility and be prepared to put in their share in the compilation of the Final Report which, with the possible exception of detailed scientific analysis, should be completed and out within six months of the return. In it, acknowledgement of all help received should be clearly shown and a further appeal made, if necessary, after declaring the successful completion of the aim and appropriate derived benefits.

THE ACCOUNT ITSELF

It is obvious but not always understood that one of the first jobs in expedition planning is to visit a Bank Manager, open an expedition account and explain what sort of expenditure is envisaged and how this is to be funded. It may be that a sizeable loan is required at the beginning and it should be realized that, although media contracts might be tied up, this does not necessarily mean that their full value will reach the account straight away. For example, book royalties and TV contracts may be phased over more than one financial year and have conditions of fulfilment by which the full price is paid only if and when the expedition's aim is achieved.

All this means that there may be considerable deficits at the beginning and at the end interest will be large. It must therefore be taken into account in budgeting unless it has been possible to obtain something like an interest free loan from one of the institutional bodies.

Usually two sets of account books are required: one for the country of origin and one for local expenditure in the country of operations. In both cases a good knowledge of accounting procedures is important and payment vouchers should be kept. In larger expeditions these accounts are audited and everything must be clearly shown.

The opening of a bank account in a foreign country can be tricky and care should be taken beforehand to ascertain how and by what method UK remittances can be received. Currency exchange controls affect the situation and Bank of England clearance may be required at this end. Some banks like Williams and Glyn's (Holts Branch) are very experienced in handling this type of account and can give expert advice. Nevertheless the problems are usually at the distant end and that is where the cash is needed. Close liaison, patience and a prearranged code of operation with the home and local branch is needed for the system to work. For example, it may become necessary to request a third party to arrange for an extra remittance. Both banks must know and honour this and control must be exercised over the number of specimen signatures given to the banks.

One problem is the physical handling and carrying of cash. It can be dangerous to arrange for a large sum of money to be drawn out in small denominations when it has to be conveyed from, say, Kathmandu to the base of a mountain or deep into the jungle for pay for local labour; and often it has to be disguised as a ration pack or something similar. When eventually it reaches the treasurer, he takes over the responsibility for its security.

If possible the best way of operating is to take to the country concerned the full allowances of traveller's cheques and get the balance remitted, being careful not to have a surplus in the local bank at the end!

Other methods such as taking sterling or dollars in cash are beneficial but dangerous. It is not really worth the risk and one is reminded that being caught can affect the whole expedition as well as future expeditions.

SELECTION OF EXPEDITION MEMBERS

The leader

Expeditions are conceived in many different ways. Sometimes it is the dream of one man which can only become reality in the hands of another. It is this second man, the potential leader, who gets the venture off the ground. Such was the case in the Darien Gap Expedition (1971–2) when author Tim Nicholson researched and dreamed of making the first complete vehicle journey from Alaska to Cape Horn. It is doubtful whether Nicholson could have led, or even wanted to lead, the expedition himself. He needed an experienced leader who could achieve his aim for him.

In the majority of cases an expedition is born by talking, questioning and acting. A small group of individuals suddenly hit upon the idea which gradually develops into a full-scale expedition. The leader usually emerges through specialist knowledge or through sheer force of personality.

Most people will join a leader who displays know-how and experience and at the same time appears objective with a balanced disposition. The problem is that while lots of people want to go on an expedition, very few are willing to assume the responsibilities of absolute leadership. It therefore becomes important that the right man is chosen at the beginning to take on the duties of leader and is aware of the administrative load involved and of the necessity to form a good team who will work with him in the planning and execution of the aim. The leader himself may well be an expert in certain fields but it is highly unlikely, and probably undesirable, that he knows everything required for his expedition. The selection of his team, therefore, becomes extremely important and can undoubtedly result in the difference between success and failure.

The team

In large-scale Himalayan expeditions the nucleus of the team is usually chosen from close friends. This was certainly so in the Annapurna and recent Everest Expeditions and highly understandable when it is realized that to know each other well beforehand and to have climbed together previously is of enormous importance later. However, it is not sufficient to have a group of close friends on any expedition. What are their qualifications? Any reasonably large expedition must have members who can fulfil certain key roles, not only on the expedition itself, but beforehand and even afterwards. It is no use having ten men who can put an ice axe on a mountain summit if the expedition never arrives at the base camp.

In addition to looking for generally desirable expedition characteristics, the leader should select his team with a view to filling the following key roles:

1. Leader
2. Deputy Leader
3. Specialist Equipment Member
4. Stores (QM) Member
5. Transport/Communications Member
6. Food Member
7. Medical Officer/Member
8. Treasurer

It may be that the Deputy Leader, who should always be officially appointed, can carry out one of the functions or that other members have, say, two roles to undertake.

The size of the team

In addition to earmarking definite spheres of responsibility, it is also important from the start to decide on a sensible format which shows the breakdown of activities and functions in the field. In very large expeditions it may be necessary to establish an elaborate line of communication backwards from the area of operations to 'civilization'. This can cover such things as medical evacuation requests, provision of local fresh food, repair and maintenance of used and broken items, mail, film and extrication of scientific samples. It may also have to handle local currency, cash remittances and situation reports to the home country as well as local authorities. It may need a sizeable staff and have to be set up before the arrival of the main party.

It is only when these sorts of things have been worked out (usually after a detailed reconnaissance), that field jobs can be earmarked and the size of the team determined. For instance, in any expedition, logistics, load carrying, communications and transportation will form a very large proportion of the man hours worked. It stands to reason, therefore, that the team on the ground should be sufficiently large and balanced to ensure that these vital tasks can be carried out. On the other hand nothing is worse than a bigger team than is necessary.

Excluding, for the moment, the rearward line of communication, it is fair to think of a normal size expedition as a football team of eleven men with, say, five forwards, three half backs and three defence. Using this analogy for an assault on a mountain, the five forwards would be the lead climbers (all capable of reaching the summit), the three half backs would constitute the support party working up to the middle or upper part of the mountain, whilst the three defence, which would probably include the doctor, Base Camp Manager and one other, would ensure that the resupply chain is maintained from the bottom. Although this is generalizing it can be seen that all expeditions will need members who, whilst ideally being capable of great versatility, can carry out a support task and not necessarily feel that they have to be out in front. It is essential to put this concept over right at the start: too many people seek what they imagine is the glory without giving thought to the majority workload further back. Indeed it is probably better to take people who readily appreciate this fact and can honestly say that they are happy to make such a contribution to the expedition, than continue detailed planning with too many experts all clamouring for eventual rewards.

Amazingly enough, it is so often from the support parties that true talent is found on the expedition itself. Time and again, when the attrition point is reached and certain of the forward sections or lead parties have burned themselves out, it is from the middle or base portion of the expedition that a leader seeks replacements. These very men have been known to reach the top or join the crucial phase of a worthwhile journey or discovery.

What about the numbers to be taken? This depends on the nature of the task, the inclusion of labour intensive personnel as opposed to the hiring of a local work force, the duration of the expedition and the scale of operations. For Annapurna it was eleven, for recent Everest expeditions it was eighteen less Sherpas, for the Darien it was sixty-five and for the Zaïre River Expedition it was over 150. It is essential to remember that expense is directly related to numbers. One side issue worth bearing in mind is that it has been found that where small self-contained groups are concerned, six people is the best number.

Individual selection

Every leader has his own way of sizing up and judging the people he selects for his expedition. The necessity for absolute experts in fields like lead climbing, medicine, scientific research, survey and logistics are obvious but even here it is worthwhile assessing a person's ability to apply his knowledge on an expedition. For example, a doctor who has worked alone or possibly abroad before and is used to making diagnoses independently, quickly and decisively, is far more use than a more highly qualified but less practical man who is normally used to referring to other doctors or a nearby hospital. Scientists, too, can be gifted expeditionists who will merge successfully into a team or they can be unaware and alien to the environment to which they are subjected.

Certain fairly obvious qualities are sought in any expedition member. These are:

Compatibility as a member of a team, Fitness, physically and mentally, Even temper and good humour, Enthusiasm for the job, Endurance and determination, Ability to accept hardships and inconvenience, Loyalty, Initiative and ability to act independently and Flexibility to change roles or jobs.

In addition, a leader should look for proficiency in such things as swimming, driving, rope and rock climbing, survival techniques, first aid and knowledge of local languages. Binding them all together must be a sense of keenness and real motivation, for it is this alone which will overcome the stresses and strains and impart the necessary team spirit.

All of these qualities should also be weighed up and judged against suitability for the task and knowledge of the job. In my opinion it is more important to have an enthusiastic all rounder whose attitude is right than to have an expert who lacks flexibility. Sometimes a compromise is called for but, above all, the individual members of any expedition must realize that they are dependent upon each other and that as a team they must know and understand the aim and be willing to work flat out to achieve it.

Girls are in no way inferior to men on expeditions. Physically, in terms of lifting heavy objects, a man might be stronger but girls can possess just as much endurance and can often add a touch of sanity to the situation. Their individual talents can add greatly to a team's result and it goes without saying that they can raise morale and, merely by being there, keep spirits up in bad situations. In my experience the tone of an expedition can be enhanced greatly by including women.

Further considerations

The selection of a team can be a very difficult job and should never be underestimated. It is a good idea to devise a comprehensive proforma which asks for details of experience, knowledge and personal data and then to conduct interviews or at least meet applicants and get to know them. It is extremely dangerous to select a member on spec and experience has shown that the more people who have known each other beforehand the better the end result. Perhaps the best solution is to arrange one or more familiarization weekends in a central location. This always pays off.

Do not forget to include reserves and in the early phases of selection mention should be made of the appropriate financial contribution expected towards the cost of the expedition. This fact alone is a very good pointer to genuine interest or band-waggoning.

Lastly, and most important, a rear party must be appointed who not only knows what is going on but is keen enough to follow the expedition in detail and respond to cries of help and urgent demands from 'the front'. Its responsibilities may include anything from postcards and philately to arranging further cash remittances, despatching airfreight items, coordinating black and white and colour film, and keeping wives and families in the picture. Remember, the rear party is in this country and acts as the base of operations. It may well be that it either forms part of or is in close liaison with the Expedition Committee but the chances are that most of the unglamorous but vital tasks are performed by this necessary agency. The selection and willing participation by the person or persons who perform this role is as important as the team itself.

DOCUMENTATION

Documentation needs to be started early and frequently takes longer than one might think.

Passports must be up-to-date and visas obtained in plenty of time. If an overland journey is being made the passport has to go to each Embassy in turn and some cannot be hurried. In the journeys involving the Middle East it may be necessary to obtain two passports, one for Israel and one for Arab countries. Normally visas are for short duration periods only and it may be more difficult to obtain a visa for, say, six months.

Some countries will ask for proof of availability of financial sources or a declaration to the effect that so much money exists per day of stay.

In the case of vehicles, a guarantor is required for a Carnet and this means finding some organization such as a bank to agree to stand the loss if a vehicle has to be abandoned in a foreign country or not re-exported. Normally the value for the Carnet is 150% of the value of the vehicle and in the case of a fitted Land-Rover or Range-Rover this can be a great deal. It is worth consulting the AA about their own Carnet scheme, but this may cost up to £100, especially if a double indemnity is taken out as an insurance against write off.

For other vehicle documentation the AA and RAC are good and helpful. Do not forget about international driving licences.

For all documentation a good tip is to have at least a dozen extra passport photographs of every expedition member.

Health restrictions and control is a matter for the leader or expedition doctor to arrange. He should co-ordinate the requirement for inoculations, list everybody's blood group and be aware of each individual member's medical history. Inoculations are normally given against some or all of the following: polio, typhoid, cholera, tetanus, smallpox, yellow fever, diphtheria and infective hepatitis.

The rear parties, both at home and at the base end of the L of C, need to know details such as next of kin, contact telephone numbers and addresses.

Insurance is of paramount importance. There should be three types:

1. Insurance for all kit and equipment, 2. Personal health and injury insurance for members, 3. Injury and death indemnity or insurance for third parties or local helpers and labour.

Most brokers will help but good cover is not always easy to find and can be extremely expensive. It is important to realize that medical costs for attention and hospitalization abroad can be incredibly expensive and no one should go without a personal accident/injury policy.

The secretarial assistance necessary to cover all of this may have to include one or two people full time. There is also the help needed for co-ordinating the lecture programme, receiving and labelling black and white and transparency film, running the philately interests and the work of handling postcards and posters. Much of this needs to continue after the expedition has left.

Most good expeditions put out a series of information reports to their members, committee, sponsors and patrons. This is a very good idea and is designed to keep everyone in the picture on progress, contracts signed, income potential, budget estimates and so on. At the same time it can specify tasks in writing, ask for information, openly declare agreed financial contributions and cover medical aspects. These reports should, ideally, be continued right until the expedition is wound up. The post-expedition reports on progress are just as necessary.

The most complicated part of documentation is for stores where import licences are required at the far end. There may also be the added difficulty of entries into a country of transit where bonds are used. An example of this is shipping goods to Bombay for road conveyance to Nepal. It is wise to find out at an early stage exactly what is required. It could be as many as fifteen copies of the manifest broken down into box contents, listed under specific categories of goods with values shown in three different currencies. The whole is then further split into consumable goods and re-export goods. Each category is charged customs at a different rate and a cheque has to be left with the customs for the chargeable value of the re-exportable items. This cheque is cancelled if and when the goods are re-exported. All of this may be needed to obtain an Import Licence without which the goods cannot be cleared through customs. This process can take time and if it goes wrong, either a lot of money can be wasted on customs or the delay can cause further expense in demurrage. Obviously the actual value of the goods declared affects the customs charge and knowledge of the various categories of customs charges is worth having. Allowance for this type of research is never wasted and if there is a reconnaissance this fact finding should be one of its tasks.

It may be as a result of this that the method of packaging before departure is amended. What is important is that the lists declared for obtaining the Import Licence are correctly matched by the box description and number. If the contents do not match the declared list on, say, the box that the customs decide to open, the whole operation is put in jeopardy.

For most of us documentation is boring and time consuming. It is also vital and its poor production can seriously affect an expedition's progress. But however good it may be, there comes a time when one or more members are left dealing with local bureaucrats. However unreasonable they may seem, the secret is to keep calm and act with tact, objective forcefulness and serene patience. Do not push too hard and never lose your temper. When all is done, say thank you and at least appear grateful.

MOVEMENTS, TRANSPORTATION AND SUPPLY

Movement to and from an expedition area is probably the biggest single headache and most expensive budgeted item.

Going by ship may be cheaper but it is longer and can take too much time away from an expedition's timetable. Sending freight by ship suffers the same problem which can be augmented if the ship arrives at a port which is not in the same country as the expedition. Documentation can be very tricky.

Air travel is always best but can work out very expensive. However, a good knowledge of the various methods of air travel such as charter, apex and off season is essential. It is only when one sees the vast difference in price for reaching the same destination that one realizes that an expedition can save or lose hundreds or thousands of pounds if insufficient research is done. Generally speaking, it is unwise to travel on a weekend and obviously July and August, being peak periods, are more expensive than other times.

Air freight can also be incredibly expensive but is obviously advantageous. Despite this it can often go wrong; either by somehow getting off loaded at the wrong airport or lost in warehouses. Demurrage can also be charged. The knowledge of air way bills is therefore very useful and whoever despatches the equipment should be advised to signal the expedition party all details on the air way bill.

Another method of transport is of course vehicle. Often this is not feasible but where expedition areas can be reached by road and ferry it is definitely the cheapest and most effective way. On the 1975 Everest expedition all the kit was sent out in two huge vehicles to Kathmandu beforehand. The previous Everest expedition spent about £20,000 in air freight. Expeditions to Africa and the Middle East can also get there satisfactorily by vehicle. Ferries too can be used, e.g. the one from Southampton to Tangier.

Within the framework of an expedition other methods of transport might be rail, hovercraft, mules or pack ponies, inflatable river craft, light aircraft or helicopter, dug-out canoes or local craft, motor vehicles, including motorcycles, cross country buggies, motorized wheelbarrows, snowmobiles, sledges, dogs and porters. All of these require fuel, specialist equipment and maintenance. Sometimes the hire of local transport is more economical than taking it from this country. In other cases where thirsty motors are involved like aircraft, hovercraft, outboard motors and vehicles the arrangements for pre-dumping supplies of fuel and its availability have to be considered very early on, preferably by the reconnaissance or advance party.

Clearances and customs

In the early stages of planning it may be necessary to obtain political clearance to enter the country. About four to six months should be allowed for. In the case of Nepal where high altitude expeditions are planned, each mountain has to be booked and the waiting list can be up to several years. For example, Everest is booked twice a year till 1982 as I write. The paperwork for clearances overlaps with the section on documentation and may include things like trek permits and specific authorities for operating in interiors. Certainly, when moving from one area to another it is worthwhile obtaining letters of authority and introductions in the local language or script. It is also worth visiting the Cultural Attachés of foreign embassies here who can advise with up to date information on such matters for their own country.

For some expeditions it may be necessary to appoint an agent at the port of entry. Failing this, knowledge of the import licence and customs procedures is essential. A whole expedition can be ruined if this aspect of administration goes wrong. The breakdown of consumable and re-export items is essential and items like aerosols, formalin, weapons, ammunition, radios, etc. must be declared properly. Customs fees should also be allowed for and could be as much as £3,000 for very large expeditions.

When leaving this country it is advisable to seek customs advice on the procedure for re-importation. Sometimes the Customs and Excise Notice to pack and Shipping Bill for goods intended for temporary exportation (Form XS 140) and Notice Number 207 on relief from customs duty and purchase tax for re-importation of goods are necessary and must be filled in.

Within the supply line

Within the concept of an L of C, it follows that the supply chain can be adapted to fit the need. The main thing to remember is that throughout an expedition, resupply is necessary and continuous. There is no rest and it is hard work. It includes fuel, food, equipment, scientific needs, mail, film, money, casualties and visitors. A forward resupply team may have to operate independently for a long period in a remote situation. It may have to rely on very accurate navigation to reach the main party and it seldom gets credit for its efforts; but it forms a vital link to the chain on which the progress of the whole expedition depends. This goes for all intermediary positions and agents between the sharp end and the base.

The base itself is rather like the bottom of a pyramid. Everything leaves it and returns to it but the further away the expedition goes from it the more difficult its task becomes. It has to be flexible and resourceful and needs a senior member of the expedition to run it.

1. Kelvin Kent explaining the food packs on the Everest South West Face Expedition of 1972. Three different types of rations were provided, each with four separate menus.

Personal movement

Whether in the jungle, in the desert, on mountains or in the Arctic, travelling alone over difficult country, especially in poor weather conditions, is dangerous and not worth it. If something goes wrong, think of the plight of the rescuers and of the extra time and manpower which is sapped from the expedition to sort it out.

PHOTOGRAPHY—BEFORE AND AFTER

Taking photographs is common sense. No one has to be an expert but it is worth being familiar with the basics, and these start before the expedition leaves.

Before

First, choose sensible equipment. Very expensive gear is fine for the professional, but not necessarily vital. The best solution is either a sturdy, easy to re-load single lens reflex camera like a Pentax, Olympus, Nikon, Canon or Leica. The only disadvantage is weight and bulk so a good alternative is one of the smaller Canon, Kodak or Rollei 35 cameras. The perfect answer is to carry both so that black and white and colour transparency film can be available together. In any case the most important quality is reliability and to achieve this it may be necessary to suggest tropicalizing in some circumstances.

Another good idea for expeditions is a Polaroid camera. The ability to produce a picture almost straight away is not only an excellent aid for local relations, but can be extremely useful for recces and briefings.

Film itself is worth organizing centrally with a proportion given out to members and the rest kept in a pool. As many of the expedition as possible should be given or encouraged to take, their own camera. This may appear a nuisance to some but in the end, it is the only way to ensure that pictures are obtainable of all areas at all times.

The type of lens selected is important. I have found a 28 or 35 mm wide angle lens perfectly acceptable but a 55 mm lens is better. For long range work a 135 mm telephoto is worth taking, and a 400 mm telephoto is ideal for birds and animals. A big lens like this can also serve as a telescope which can be very useful indeed. Lastly, a UV filter is always a safe bet and apart from its primary function, does protect the lens itself.

A lightweight tripod, a repair kit, spare batteries for light meters and flash equipment, a cable release with spare cables and a set of plastic bags or covers for protection against water and dust, are worth thinking about and taking.

After

Co-ordination is required to ensure that the pictures are used to best effect. There may be a book, magazine articles, a lecture set and advertising pictures before individuals can claim their own pictures back. On top of this it may be wise to contact one of the many picture and photographic agencies who accept good pictures and sell them at attractive prices.

Most important of all is the need to have a system of addressing, labelling and numbering individual films in separate colour slide and black and white containers. Ideally, these should be sent back during the expedition to the rear party who can label individuals' films and get them processed. Slides are straightforward but each one should be matched with the photographer's initials and black and white should be produced on contact prints first. For this system to work, a good quantity of appropriate bags and labels must be taken on the expedition.

Individual photographers should try to keep a diary of their shots. Afterwards, when checking through, it pays to be ruthless and throw out any marginal shot or picture where the focus or exposure is wrong. A few good pictures are better than a lot of bad ones.

It is also worth remembering that in practice, taking a photograph can be quite an effort, especially in times of stress and fatigue. Often, people don't like having their picture taken when they are worn out. Nevertheless, the extra effort and willpower needed to get the camera out and take the picture under these circumstances is justified and nearly always successful.

Lastly, although not photographic it is perhaps appropriate to mention the usefulness of sketches. Apart from adding another interesting medium in description, it is amazing how well received a reasonable sketch is afterwards and for the report. Most important, of course, are sketch maps and drawings of local people and their surroundings.

See Appendix (p. 236) for lists of essential kit and equipment.

2. EXPEDITION HEALTH AND MEDICINE

by Peter Steele

The unprepared and the unwary are those for whom expeditions abroad can end in misery and expense ('when a party becomes labelled an expedition it means there are a lot too many people'— Tilman). Not only may the sick member fall by the wayside but the entire trip may be put in jeopardy involving huge wastage of money, time and opportunity. Illness can often be avoided by adequate preparation beforehand and common sense precautions during the journey. In this chapter I am not trying to offer you a complete medical compendium, rather a guide to preventing the common hazards of travelling abroad, with reference to the main problems of widely differing geographical situations.

It is always comforting to have a doctor along but do not be lulled into false security. A doctor is of use only in proportion to what he knows and understands about the medical problems of the highly specialized environment in which you are travelling. Just because he has MB, or whatever, after his name does not mean he is any more use than a competent traveller who has bothered to learn the elements of the trade as it concerns a sick man in wild places.

Fitness

I am not a physical training fiend since, by having the good fortune to be of lean build and by taking a moderate amount of exercise, I keep a steady level of fitness. I can see little point in training madly before an expedition unless you are grossly out of

2. Peter Steele examining a team member at the base hospital on the International Everest Expedition of 1971.

shape (if you are in such a state you probably will not be invited anyway); one attack of diarrhoea will reduce athletic muscles to jelly in a few hours. However you should see that you are in reasonable health, and the exercise that will be an inescapable part of your journey will fix the rest.

MEDICAL PRELIMINARIES

Before embarking on an expedition you would be wise to have a thorough medical check-up and certain tests, not only to see that you are fit, but also to have a baseline for comparison should you fall ill later. You do not have to be tough and hairy to go on an expedition or be a good outdoorsman—some of the greatest explorers were written off as weaklings in their youth. Leaders should beware of excluding good men because of doubtful medical records that may be no longer relevant.

The examination should include:

1. Past medical history

Serious illnesses, operations (particularly appendicectomy) and drug sensitivity or contact allergy.

Personal medical details can be imprinted on a bracelet or medallion that must be worn constantly (Medic-Alert, 43a Wigmore Street, London W1H 9LE). This is safer than a card carried in the pocket or wallet, and may be life-saving in an emergency.

e.g. Blood group—in case blood transfusion is needed after an accident.
Drug treatment dosage—for diabetics, epileptics and those taking steroids or other medicines.
Sensitivity—to specific drugs, e.g. penicillin, sulphonamides, aspirin.
Allergies—to bites, stings and pollens.

2. General physical examination

Together with these tests; urine analysis, haemoglobin and blood group, chest X-ray and T.B. tests.

3. Dental check

Remember to take with you:

Medicines with which you are already being treated. The dosage and pharmocological name should be written on the bottle since proprietary names vary in different countries.

Spare spectacles and your lens prescription.

In many countries long hair is synonymous with hippies and undeserved rough handling may be given by the police and government officials. Apart from which long hair is difficult to keep clean.

VD is never caught off cracked cups or lavatory seats but it is sometimes carried unknowingly, particularly by women. Local 'groupies' 'who provide creature comforts that are lacking during an expedition' have introduced new hazards. Any man who, having put himself at risk, has a discharge from the penis and passes water painfully and often should go for an immediate check-up and warn his girlfriend to do likewise.

Insurance

Falling ill abroad can be very expensive. The European Economic Community (EEC) Belgium, Denmark, France, West Germany, Ireland, Italy, Luxembourg and the Netherlands, have reciprocal arrangements with our own National Health Service. The detailed workings of the scheme are laid out in Form SA.28, issued by the Department of Health and Social Security. This explains how the certificate of entitlement to medical treatment (Form E.III) may be obtained. It is not available to self-employed or unemployed persons. (Students beware!)

Similar arrangements for free medical care exist in Bulgaria, Poland, Norway, Sweden and Yugoslavia. When in doubt the embassies of these countries should be consulted for details.

Elsewhere the cost of consultation, medicines, treatment and hospital care must be paid for by the patient. As this could be financially crippling, full health insurance is a wise precaution. You should consult a reputable company for advice on the policies available.

Insurance covers the cost of medical treatment abroad or of flying the sick person home—this may be safest and cheapest in the long run.

Don't forget to insure every member of the party.

If you incur medical expenses, present your policy to the

doctor and ask him to send the bill direct to your insurance company; if you pay cash, keep a receipt which will be honoured on your return.

If you are going to take part in 'high-risk sports' you will need a more specific insurance cover. You should consult a company who specialize in this field and will give you an individual quote.

Foreign travel

IMMUNIZATION

When travelling abroad you can be protected by immunization against certain infectious diseases common in tropical and subtropical countries. Inoculation with a small amount of the organism or a purified derivative of the toxin that causes the disease, though not enough to give you the disease, stimulates your body to produce immune antibodies that mop up stray and dangerous bugs.

Protection against typhoid, paratyphoid and tetanus is an advisable safeguard wherever you go abroad, and inoculations can be done by your family doctor. Immunization against poliomyelitis, diphtheria and tuberculosis is given to most schoolchildren and need not be repeated, but you should check that this was done during childhood.

In certain foreign countries immunization against smallpox, yellow fever and cholera is compulsory by international agreement, and you have to show a valid up-to-date international certificate at the place of entry. This can apply to short stopovers while in transit during the main journey. The certificate has to be on an approved form, signed and dated by the doctor who inoculated you, and stamped by the local authority of your area. You will also have to produce valid international certificates when returning to the United Kingdom from most countries abroad. The embassy of the country concerned will give you the most recent information on inoculation requirements. If in doubt about any aspects of immunization enquire at your District Community Physician's Department (Public Health Department).

INJURY AND TRAUMA

Accidents are likely in any of the situations we are discussing as they carry a higher risk than normal living. However the management of airway block or a broken leg is basically the same whether it happens on the deck of a boat, on the side of a mountain or in the middle of the desert. In this chapter there is no space to deal with the subject of such trauma; if you want a book to carry with you that gives a comprehensive account of 'first aid' in expedition situations, I suggest you read my book *Medical Care for Mountain Climbers* (see page 73) and adapt the information to the geography concerned.

The principle of emergency medical care in remote regions is to prevent the injured person dying before he reaches skilled help, to make sure the injury does not worsen in the meantime by inept handling, and to relieve pain and apprehension.

A. Unconsciousness and airway block

The causes range from drowning to head injury, diabetes to epilepsy. The airway from the mouth to the lungs must be prevented from becoming blocked by the tongue falling backwards and acting like a cork stopper. Place the victim in the 'draining position', lying on his side with the head lower than the chest in order to allow secretions—blood or vomit—to drain away from the lungs. Hold the chin forward to prevent the tongue falling back and blocking the airway. If breathing stops completely you may have to give mouth-to-mouth assisted breathing; if the heart stops chest compression may be needed to keep the circulation to the brain and vital organs going.

B. Injury

Nature is a wonderful healer if given adequate encouragement. *Cuts and grazes* go septic quickly so must be taken seriously. Wash thoroughly with soap and water or an antiseptic solution (gentian violet or potassium permanganate). Cover with a sterile plaster strip or non-stick ('Melolin') gauze. Antiseptic cream may be used if the wound is difficult to clean adequately, but it tends to make the dressing stick and keeps the wound moist, which delays healing. Anchor dressings are useful for awkward places, i.e. fingers, heels. If the cut is clean and gaping bring the edges together with 'Steristrips' in place of stitches.

Deep wounds: firm pressure on a wound dressing will stop most bleeding. If blood seeps through put more dressing on top, secured with absorbent crepe bandage, and keep up the pressure, elevating the part if possible.

Burns: superficial burns are simply skin wounds. Leave open to the air to form a dry crust under which healing goes on. If this is not possible cover with 'Melolin' dressings. Burn creams offer no magic. Deep burns must be kept scrupulously clean and treated urgently by a doctor. Give drinks freely to replace lost fluid.

Sprains: apply a firm crepe or elastoplast bandage. If painful movement and swelling persist, suspect a fracture. Cold compresses help reduce swelling.

Fractures: immobilize the part by splinting to a rigid structure; the arm can be strapped to the chest, both legs can be tied together. Temporary splints can be made from a rolled newspaper, an ice axe or a branch. Pain may be agonizing and is due to movement of broken bone ends on each other.

C. Pain

Pain-killers fall into three strengths for different grades of pain:

mild—Aspirin (lowers the temperature but can irritate the stomach); Paracetamol is a useful alternative.

moderate—Pentazocine 'Fortral' (can cause hallucinations).
severe—Pethidine, Morphine (may depress the breathing dangerously. Only available on special prescription).

PRECAUTIONS AGAINST INFECTIOUS ORGANISMS

Water and food are the most common sources of disease because they become polluted by infected faeces and urine of a carrier, e.g. typhoid, dysentery, cholera, schistosomiasis, hookworm. Generally speaking people in tropical countries are less discriminating about where they defecate, partly owing to ignorance, partly to lack of adequate latrines. Germs from an infected person may directly contaminate the drinking water supplies, or are carried to food by flies. These diseases are prevented by drinking only pure water, eating clean food and disposing of sewerage efficiently.

A. Drinking

1. WATER

Infected drinking water causes many diseases. If in doubt about the water, purify it yourself. Water taken direct from the taps is best avoided and certain towns (e.g. Kathmandu) are notorious for polluted civil water supplies. Hillside springs well clear of human habitation and animal grazing should be safe, but stream and river water is likely to be polluted. Glacial mud and mica that give Alpine rivers their murky appearance often upset the gut.

Water purification

1. Boiling. Boiling briskly for a few minutes kills most organisms (including amoeba cysts and infectious hepatitis virus) and is the only way water can be truly 'sterilized'. The colour, taste and smell of water are immaterial provided it has been boiled. (This

may be a problem at high altitude where the boiling point is lower than at sea-level so boiling takes longer and is less efficient.) A wise rule is to drink tea or coffee that has been made with boiling water.

2. Chemical Treatment. Chlorine is the basic ingredient of most water-purifying tablets, which are useful for disinfecting water-borne bacteria, but will not touch amoeba cysts or bacteria embedded in solid particles. Iodine kills amoeba cysts as well as bacteria.

When large quantities of water have to be prepared and boiling is not practicable, purifying tablets, which can be bought from any chemist, can be put in the water bottles, but they leave a taste of chlorine. The directions for use are printed on the bottle.

3. Filtration. Filters (Milipore, Katadyn, Millbank Filter bag) remove suspended matter and some bacteria, giving the water a deceptively clear appearance. They are useful for cleaning large amounts of water but are the least reliable way of making it pure. Filters have to be kept scrupulously clean or they lose their value. Water should be boiled after filtration not before.

2. DRINKS

Bottled fizz, iced drink cubes and ice-lollies are only as safe as the water from which they are made. Milk must be boiled if not pasteurized; powdered milk is safe if made up with boiled water but should then only be kept in a refrigerator. Wine drunk in moderation is harmless but a surfeit upsets the stomach. Spirits have to be taken in excessive amounts in order to kill any germs; there are more efficient but possibly less pleasant ways of doing this.

3. ICE CREAM

Germs are harboured in ice cream, both from the ingredients and from subsequent handling. Well advertised brands cannot afford to lose their reputation by slackness in their preparation and so should be reasonably safe.

B. Food

Freshly and thoroughly cooked food is safe since any bacteria will have been killed by the heat; so avoid pre-cooked and handled food, especially where flies abound. Peel all fruit and vegetables; thorough washing is only second best so beware of salads, tomatoes, lettuces and especially watercress because human nightsoil is often used as a fertilizer in the tropics. Washing food in a strong solution of potassium permanganate for about five minutes is wise but not infallible. Meat should be thoroughly cooked and eaten immediately, as raw or underdone beef and pork harbour tapeworms. Risk shell-fish and inadequately cleaned prawns only if you have a tough stomach.

You have to strike a balance between making life a misery through worrying about what you eat and drink and taking commonsense precautions. You cannot shield your gut from every conceivable germ, and some early contact, with its resulting dose of the 'runs', is inevitable to allow yourself to build up immunity that will protect you from further attacks.

C. Hygiene

Many toilets are dirty; you may have to squat and keep your balance by holding on to the walls. Take your own toilet paper as newsprint is rough and fragile. Wash your hands carefully with soap as soon as possible afterwards. Remember, dirty lavatories = dirty kitchens.

Brush your teeth in boiled water only. Chewing gum is a useful temporary freshener when clean water is scarce.

COMMON INFECTIONS

A. Traveller's diarrhoea

Known as 'food poisoning' or 'gastro-enteritis', *this illness causes more trouble to the traveller than all the other medical hazards abroad put together*. It has as many local names (Gippy Tummy, Delhi Belly, Kathmandu Quickstep, Tokyo Trots, Rangoon Runs, Montezuma's Revenge) as patent remedies. The causes are usually untraceable but may include gluttony, change in climate, and an upset in the bacteria that are normal and necessary in the bowel. Frank infection with disease-causing organisms carried in water and food is less common.

Much pleasure in travelling abroad comes from eating local food and drinking wine; it is hardly worth going all that way for beer, fish and chips. But eat and drink in moderation in order to avoid what could turn out to be a very expensive tummy upset that will spoil your journey.

TREATMENT

Traveller's diarrhoea is usually a self-limiting illness that clears in two to three days. You may vomit and feel groggy because of dehydration due to loss of body water. Go to bed and drink unlimited fluids (at least a pint an hour of plain boiled water or tea). Avoid eating except dried toast, peeled grated apple turned brown (pectin) or kaolin powder. A short period of starvation can do you no harm and the idea that you must 'give the stomach something to work on' is nonsense.

The 'Everest Blunderbuss Cocktail' constipates most people for a week.

Recipe
Kaolin powder 2 tablespoonfuls.

Codeine phosphate 15 mg 2–4 tablets.
Diphenoxylate ('Lomotil') 4–6 tablets.
Tincture of morphine ('Chlorodyne') 4–6 drops (sleepy-making).

Antibiotics should *not* be used blindly since they kill normal bacteria, which are protective, as well as poison-producing ones; they play little part in speeding recovery and may prolong the excretion of bugs during convalescence. Many popular brands of diarrhoea medicine are at best useless, at worst potentially dangerous.

If diarrhoea does not stop on this treatment, or if blood appears in the stools, consult a doctor. If this is impossible because of geographical isolation, the best initial drug is co-trimoxazole ('Septrin', 'Bactrim') 2 tablets twice daily or a simple sulphonamide—phthalylsulphathalazole, 1 gm four times daily.

B. Dysentery

Infection of the bowel with bacteria or amoeba can only be diagnosed accurately by examining the stool under the microscope and by growing the offending organism. Antibiotic sensitivity can then be tested and the appropriate drug prescribed.

1. *Bacillary Dysentery.* Salmonella, shigella (which also causes typhoid) and staphylococci are the usual organisms of the disease, which is commoner than amoebic dysentery.

The onset is acute and severe. The temperature rises quickly to 38°–39°C and the patient feels sick but usually does not vomit. He has urgent, explosive diarrhoea that may contain blood and mucus, and cramps in his abdomen. Consult a doctor who may prescribe sulpha drugs or chloramphenicol (many doctors who have not suffered themselves may disapprove of this useful drug).

2. *Amoebic Dysentery*. Amoebic dysentery is much rarer and has a more gradual onset than bacillary dysentery and may take more than a month to develop. Each day three to four loose foul-smelling stools are passed increasing to a dozen with blood, a lot of mucus, and painful straining and colic.

Metronidizole ('Flagyl') is the drug of choice. 500 mg three times daily.

C. Typhoid (enteric) fever

Infection is caused by the germ salmonella typhi. Fever increases in a spiky fashion over several weeks, with bloody diarrhoea and headache. Eventually the patient is prostrate and desperately ill.

Medical help is urgently needed. Chloramphenicol is the recommended drug; prednisone taken for a week reduces the symptoms rapidly and makes the dangerous complication of perforation of the bowel less likely.

D. Cholera

Cholera was epidemic throughout the world in 1973, notably in parts of Southern Europe. The cholera organisms come only from the human intestine and are spread by faecally contaminated water, not by direct contact or inhalation. Shellfish collect the germs and are particularly dangerous when eaten raw.

A sudden onset of profuse watery diarrhoea with cramps and ultimate collapse due to dehydration (which can all happen within a few hours) in a known epidemic area calls for immediate attention at hospital.

Fluid should be replaced by intravenous drip, whenever possible. The antibiotics of choice are tetracycline and chloramphenicol.

E. Worms

Most worms can be prevented by careful hygiene and by boiling drinking water. An itchy bottom is often the first warning; look carefully for the worm, or part of it, in your stool. Usually one dose of the appropriate drug cleans out the worms.

1. *Roundworms and Threadworms.* These worms are easily seen. They can mimic appendicitis and, as this is rare in dwellers in the tropics, doctors should beware of wielding the knife unnecessarily.

Drug. Piperazine ('Pripsen'). 4 gm immediately.

2. *Tapeworms.* Tapeworms thrive in under-cooked beef, pork and fish. Segments of the worm are passed in the stool, but the head remains attached to the gut and must be killed to prevent it growing again.

Drug. Dichlorophen ('Antiphen').

3. *Hookworms.* Larvae enter through abrasions in the feet, so you should wear shoes in an infected area. Blood in the stool and anaemia occur.

Drug. Bephenium granules ('Alcopar'). 5 gm immediately.

4. *Bilharzia (Schistosomiasis).* The fluke lives in fresh water in Africa, central America and Japan. It enters your body when you drink infected water or through your feet, so beware of paddling or drinking from slow-flowing rivers and lakes. The veins of the bladder are its favourite haunt so passing blood in the urine is a danger sign; diarrhoea and itching are frequent.

Drugs—should be under supervision of a doctor.

F. Constipation

Constipation is rarely a problem when travelling abroad. Drink plenty and eat fruit and roughage; if this does not help take a laxative. In desperation give an enema by passing a pint of soapy solution into the rectum using a well-greased rubber tube and a funnel.

G. Infectious hepatitis

This virus infection is usually carried in faeces and acquired from infected food and water, or by swimming near a sewage outlet. Jaundice, a yellow discoloration of the skin most easily noticed in the whites of the eyes, is preceded by a vague and unpleasant malaise for two to three weeks, and the person often feels better once the jaundice has appeared.

No preventive immunization exists. Gamma (Immuno-) globulin gives some protection if given within two weeks of exposure to the virus, so should be reserved for recent contacts and not given as long-term protection.

H. Malaria

Anopheline mosquitoes transmit parasites which cause malaria. The symptoms are high fevers, shivering, aching and sweats. No immunization is possible against malaria. Although it has been eradicated from many parts of the world there are still large areas of the tropics where malaria is endemic. The Anopheline species carries malaria and tends to bite around dusk. Discourage them from biting by wearing long sleeves and trousers, by using insect repellent and sleeping under mosquito netting at night. But you cannot entirely avoid bites and it only takes one bite from an infected mosquito to pass on malaria. So anti-malarial medicines are the only true protection.

Prophylactic anti-malarial drugs suppress malarial parasites introduced into the blood stream provided the concentration of drug is kept high enough by regular use.

Opposite is a schedule of anti-malarial prevention.

NB

Drugs should be taken with liquid after a meal.

Start taking anti-malarial drugs one week before arriving in the malarial area, take them throughout the visit, and continue for four to six weeks after returning home.

Although taking a drug weekly is convenient, you are less likely to forget a daily dose if it becomes a habit like cleaning your teeth. One single omission interrupts the protective effect, so forgetting a weekly dose could be serious.
Even making a brief stop-over in a malarial country you need full protection.
Ask a doctor on arrival what is the best prophylactic drug for the area in case there is a particularly virulent or resistant local species. You may be advised to double the dose if there is.

ANTI-MALARIAL PREVENTION SCHEDULE

Name trade name	*tablet strength*	*number freq.*	*minimum time before departure*
Proguanil (Paludrine)	100 mg	1 daily	1 day
Pyrimethamine (Daraprim)	25 mg	1 weekly	1 day
Chloroquine (Nivaquine)	100 mg	3 weekly	1 day

If you develop an unexplained fever in the tropics or after return, consult a doctor and ask for a blood film examination. This should be done especially on returning home from a malarious area. (The Ross Institute of Tropical Hygiene, Keppel Street, London WC1E 7HT.) Always tell a doctor you may have to consult that you have recently been in the tropics.

Sun

1. SUNBURN

The sun can be a stealthy enemy; it reflects strongly off water, sand and snow, and burning rays can penetrate hazy cloud and are more powerful the higher the altitude. Those with fair skin, red hair or freckles are prone to sunburn, but people vary in the speed with which they tan; tanned skin is the best protection. Ideally allow yourself less than an hour in the sun the first day and increase the time gradually. Falling asleep in the sun is a sure way to fry yourself.

Sun creams and lotions act as a screen to bar the ultraviolet rays from the skin; none of them speed sun tan. They may reduce burning (and tanning at the same time) but with excessive sun they merely act as fat in the process of frying. Rationing sunlight on your skin, especially unaccustomed areas, is cheaper and more effective. A wide-brimmed hat and a beard give good protection, but lips and noses burn easily and need cover, especially on the underside, from ultraviolet light reflection off snow.

Several 'ultraviolet barrier', sunscreens, and glacier creams are available:

Para-aminobenzoic esters ('Spectraban', 'Soltan').
Mexenone ('Uvistat').
'Sylvasun' tablets contain Vitamin A which antagonizes Vitamin D and encourages excessive formation of Vitamin D which protects the skin from burning sunlight, without reducing tanning.

If the skin goes shrimp-pink and feels prickly and hot, stay in the shade or wear a hat or loose clothing when it is necessary to go out in the sun. Calamine is soothing; lotion has a cooling effect but is not as convenient as cream. Anti-histamines allay itching but may be soporific; anti-histamine creams should not be used because of sensitivity reactions. If the skin turns bright lobster and blisters it is badly burnt and a cream containing a steroid is useful.

Treat blisters in the usual way but make sure they remain clean. If a severe general body upset with headache, vomiting and fainting develops due to sunburn, the patient should go to bed and keep cool.

2. PRICKLY HEAT

An uncomfortable, itching heat rash develops in sweaty places where air is excluded (armpits, elbow angles, groins, backs of knees) or where clothing is tight or rubs the skin.

Wear loose clothing and a light bed cover at night. Shower frequently, using soap, and dry carefully. A dusting powder (boric acid, zinc oxide) or calamine lotion relieves itching. Alcohol encourages skin vessels to dilate and makes itching worse.

3. HEAT CRAMP AND HEAT EXHAUSTION

This usually follows heavy and prolonged exercise in unacclimatized new arrivals to sudden heat and is caused by not taking sufficient water and salt to balance losses in sweating. Tiredness, cramps and vomiting are warning signs of impending collapse. The skin becomes dry and inelastic, the tongue is like sandpaper and the urine scanty, cloudy and a deep yellow-brown colour, indicating dehydration.

Drink large amounts of fluid and take salt as taste dictates when in the tropics. Food seems tasteless until enough salt has been added; concentrated salt tablets should be unnecessary. Avoid alcohol.

If someone has collapsed and cannot drink, fluid can be given by enema in large volumes with absolute safety as the body will only absorb the amount it requires.

Cool the victim slowly over about one hour as too sudden cooling can be dangerous, and if possible monitor his rectal temperature throughout. Icepacks, tepid sponging, fanning and wrapping in a wet sheet are all methods of cooling. Aspirin lowers the temperature.

If the person has recently returned from a malarious area remember the possibility that his high temperature may be due to malignant tertian malaria.

4. SUNSTROKE/HEATSTROKE

When the body gets too hot its heat-regulating mechanism fails, sweating ceases and the temperature rises far above normal because the casualty cannot lose heat fast enough. He becomes acutely short of water and feels thirsty, dizzy and sick; the skin feels hot and dry. Without treatment, the casualty's temperature may rise above 41°C (106°F) and he becomes confused and may have convulsions; above 43°C (110°F) he is likely to slip into coma and die. This serious illness warrants urgent medical help, but first of all, cool the patient rapidly.

Skin (fungus infections)

1. ATHLETE'S FOOT

Scales and cracks begin in the clefts between the small toes and the skin becomes white and moist. Itching is awful.

Carefully wash and dry between the toes with a towel kept exclusively for your own use. Powder the feet with an anti-fungal powder ('Mycota', 'Mycil', 'Tinneafax') but cream may be better in the acute stages of the infection. Use open sandals, but if socks are necessary wear cotton rather than nylon, and change them frequently.

2. DHOBIE ITCH

The groin is infected by the same fungus, and the area is red, clearly edged and itches badly.

Treat as above reading 'groin' for 'feet'.

Bites

1. ANIMALS

After any animal bite, however small, you should have a tetanus toxoid booster. In the tropics rabies must always be considered.

Rabies. Though dogs are the commonest vectors, foxes,

wolves, cats, bats and various other animals can carry the rabies virus. The virus only enters humans through a break in the skin. It lives in the saliva of an infected animal whose nervous system becomes affected, causing the frothing associated with mad dogs.

If bitten or licked by a suspect animal wash the wound with copious soap and water, but not so vigorously as to break the skin. If the wound is left open to the sun, ultraviolet light may kill any virus remaining after washing.

A course of anti-rabies vaccine with daily injections into the skin of the abdomen lasts two weeks, so will not be undertaken lightly. The suspected animal should, if possible, be caged to see if it develops signs of rabies. If it is alive ten days after the suspicious bite the patient cannot have rabies. If the animal shows signs of illness let it die or kill it and have the brain examined by a laboratory for rabies virus within 24 hours.

There is no known treatment for rabies and once truly diagnosed there is no hope of recovery.

2. SNAKES

If snakes are known to be in the area, wear boots, examine them and your sleeping bag before climbing in, and use a torch in the dark. Snakes only attack people when frightened or provoked. Only bites from poisonous snakes cause dangerous poisoning, and only one out of ten people bitten by poisonous snakes dies.

If someone is bitten take him to the local hospital which will probably keep anti-venom against the local varieties of poisonous snake. Kill the snake for accurate identification if you can. In the meantime try to reduce the amount of venom entering the circulating blood. Wash the bite thoroughly with soap and water. If a hospital is more than an hour away or if the limb starts to swell, immediately tie a handkerchief or other constricting bandage above and below the bite to close off veins and lymph vessels that return blood, and hence poison, to the heart. The 'tourniquet' must not be tight enough to occlude arteries and it must be released every half hour. The toes and fingers should remain pink and warm. Forget old wives' tales, and do not cut the skin over the bite or urinate on it.

Carry the victim so that his circulation is not speeded by exercise; splint the bitten limb and keep it dependent to localize the poison.

Anti-venom is horse serum that neutralizes the injected poison; it can cause severe reactions so must be reserved for potentially serious bites.

If cobra venom has been spat in the eyes, wash them out with copious water.

Pain must be treated and reassurance given as snake bites strike terror into the heart of even the most courageous person.

3. WASPS AND BEES

Stings from both these can be extremely painful and shocking. The stings of wasps are relieved by vinegar, of bees by bicarbonate of soda. In a sensitive person an acute reaction (anaphylaxis) can follow a sting; this is a medical emergency.

4. SCORPIONS AND SPIDERS

These bites are more venomous than wasp or bee stings. Emetine or local anaesthetic injected into the area gives rapid relief.

5. LEECHES

Leeches are troublesome in rain forests and tropical marshes. The first sign may be a bootful of blood at the end of the day since the bite is painless and contains a substance that prevents clotting. Leeches find their way into the most carefully laced boots so open sandals may be an advantage as they can be seen early. Salt or a lighted cigarette makes the leech drop off; do not pull them off or the head will be left in the wound.

6. BLACK FLY

Black flies are so tiny they penetrate mosquito netting, and give a vicious bite out of proportion to their size. They are world-wide but particularly troublesome in subarctic regions. No protection is available.

7. FLEAS

Fleas cause intense itching and a trail of bites usually left around the midriff. They have brown bodies flattened from front to the back, which is bristled.

8. LICE

Lice are small grey creatures that live in hair and clothing. If you search hard the eggs can be seen attached to the roots of hairs on the head or in the pubic area.

9. BEDBUGS

Bedbugs bite and smell, though they do not carry disease.

10. SCABIES

The mites that cause scabies tunnel between the fingers and at other creases. They are often recognized by the scratch marks caused by the intense itching and tiny red spots at the point of entry. Benzyl benzoate kills the mites in the skin.

Insects

INSECTICIDES

Crystals of powder or droplets of spray stick to the insect and slowly paralyse it. The clothing and the person must be treated. The best insecticides contain:

DDT
HCH ('Gammexane').

INSECT REPELLENTS

These are applied to the skin and are effective for a maximum of four hours, after which they need to be reapplied. The best repellents contain:

DET (Diethyl toluamide) 'Flypel', 'Skeet-o-stick'.
DMP (Dimethyl phthalate) 'Dimp'.
DBP (Dibutyl phthalate).

ANTI-ITCH

Itching can almost literally drive you crazy; the more you scratch the more you itch. Scratching with dirty finger nails is likely to turn a bite septic.

1. Calamine lotion is more soothing than the cream, but is more bulky to carry.
2. Anti-histamines all have a powerful anti-itch effect but are also soporific; chlorpheniramine ('Piriton') less than most. Beware of anti-histamine creams as they sensitize the skin to anti-histamine medicines taken later, and a violent skin reaction may result.
3. Steroid cream ('Betnovate', 'Synalar') is also effective against itching if other methods fail.

ALLERGY

Severe allergic (anaphylactic) reactions may follow bites, stings or injections to which the person is sensitive. The patient may begin with the mild symptoms of the bite but rapidly becomes shocked with severe tightness in the chest and wheezing, and abdominal pain that makes him vomit.

Hydrocortisone (100 mg) should be injected, if possible, into a vein and the patient treated for shock. Adrenaline is a good drug in competent hands but it has dangerous effects on the heart if not carefully administered.

Eyes

Painful red eyes, commonly caused by conjunctivitis, corneal abrasions, foreign bodies and ultraviolet burns, are the source of great discomfort. If you can see a foreign body, anaesthetize the cornea and remove the speck with cotton wool rolled onto a stick. All these conditions can be safely treated with antibiotic ointment, by dilating the pupil with homatropine, and applying a pad and bandage.

Snowblindness is caused by an ultraviolet burn of the cornea. Sunlight reflects strongly off snow, light-coloured rocks and sand; its rays can penetrate hazy cloud and they become more powerful the higher you climb. The result is intense pain so the eyes are screwed up tightly and such swelling of the conjunctiva and blistering of the cornea that the victim becomes temporarily 'blind'.

Snowblindness can be prevented by wearing goggles with side-shields to exclude glare, or dark glasses; horizontal slits cut in a piece of cardboard tied round the head will suffice in an emergency.

COLD CLIMATES

Cold is determined by the combined effect of air temperature and wind speed—the 'wind-chill'. You can be colder on a wet day on Dartmoor or down a cave than when the sun is shining on a windless day at the North Pole; the Western Cwm of Everest can be like a furnace or a freezer depending on the wind.

People living in Arctic and Antarctic regions avoid trouble by wearing protective clothing and by being constantly aware of the dangers of cold. Sherpas, Andean Indians and Eskimos adapt to their cold and hostile environment by knowing how to survive and how to look after themselves by intuition and experience.

A. Exposure

Mountain Hypothermia occurs when the temperature of the central core of the body falls below about 35°C owing to the combined effect of wind, wet and cold. Exhaustion and low morale worsen it. If someone behaves in an uncharacteristic manner—apathetic, stumbling, swearing, uncontrolled shivering—be on your guard. He may suddenly collapse and die.

Stop and shelter the victim, i.e. tent, polythene bag, lean-to. Re-warm him by skin-to-skin contact. Dress him in dry spare clothes and put him in a sleeping bag. Give hot drinks and a nip of alcohol can do no harm and may give him the boost he needs to get down by himself after he is rested and rewarmed. If his condition does not improve you will have to call help to evacuate him by stretcher.

When at base he should be slowly rewarmed in a water bath at 42–44°C.

B. Frostbite

Frostbite should not occur if you are clothed properly and take commonsense precautions. If you get very cold, rewarm the part quickly against warm flesh (someone else's if possible). Do *not* rub it or you will damage the skin and cause further wounding which may become infected.

Drugs which dilate the blood vessels (Vasodilators) have no specific action against frostbite although they make you feel a warm glow inside. This can be very dangerous as you are losing heat from the rest of your body and you may be tipped into Exposure.

If a foot is frozen it is better to walk on it back to a low camp where you can rapidly rewarm it in water 42–44°C. Thereafter the victim must be carried.

C. High altitude ills

Up to 12,000 ft you have little to fear—no more than on an ordinary mountain walking holiday. If you are not shaping up too well reconsider the wisdom of climbing any higher for you are entering the realm of the high, thin, cold, dry air. Slow ascent is the secret of easy acclimatization to altitude. Breathing and heartbeat speed up, a thumping headache and nausea make you feel miserable. At night sleep is elusive ('Diazepam' 5 mg). You may notice a peculiar irregularity in the pattern of breathing (Cheyne Stokes respiration) when, for a short period, breathing appears to have stopped and then gradually increases in stepwise fashion until it eventually falls off again. The normal output of urine may be diminished and very dilute.

The unpleasant symptoms of acclimatization usually pass off in a few days, but they may develop into Acute Mountain Sickness. This rarely starts below 15,000 ft so is unlikely in the Alps but may occur in Africa, the Andes or Himalayas.

If you begin to feel more ill than you would expect for your own degree of fitness and acclimatization, go down quickly and stay down rather than battle on for glory—and end up under a pile of stones on the glacier. Acute Mountain Sickness can quickly develop into High Altitude Pulmonary (lung) Oedema, or Cerebral (brain) Oedema, i.e. swelling due to abnormal retention of water. Women are more susceptible in the days before their periods. This is a potentially lethal disease the cause of which is not understood, but it can affect all ages, the fit and the unfit, those who have risen quickly and those who have not.

If someone suddenly feels, and looks, puffy in the face, goes blue round the lips, has bubbly breathing and even pink frothy sputum, evacuate them urgently to a lower altitude. Oxygen (if available) and a diuretic drug Frusemide ('Lasix') may help to clear water from the lungs; but they are no substitute for rapid descent which has a miraculous effect. Those who have suffered once are likely to do so again, so must beware.

Thrombosis

Persistent deep calf tenderness and a slight fever and pain—more than a muscular ache—may indicate a vein thrombosis. Women on the Pill are especially at risk. You should rest, preferably with the legs bandaged and elevated, and start an antibiotic. This is a serious illness so descend and seek medical advice.

Piles

Piles commonly trouble people at high altitude, probably due to raising the pressure inside the abdomen by overbreathing while carrying heavy loads. A haemorrhoidal suppository ('Anusol') gives temporary relief.

Dry cough

This is eased by inhaling steam. Codeine Phosphate 15 mg dampens it. In a violent bout of coughing you can fracture a rib; the agony may make you think you have had a heart attack but the chances of this are slim.

MEDICAL SUPPLIES

The medical supplies you carry will be decided by the size of the party, the type of country you are travelling in and your ability to use them; a doctor on a Himalayan expedition and a lone ocean sailor have very different needs. Whatever your choice try to spread your medical equipment among several members of the party as the kit is invariably in the wrong place at the time it is most urgently needed.

Each person should have his own small, individual medical kit, packed in a waterproof box that stays with him. The leader of a small party carries a larger box with more variety of equipment. On an expedition where the party may be widely dispersed, a camp medical box should stay in the tents and never be taken

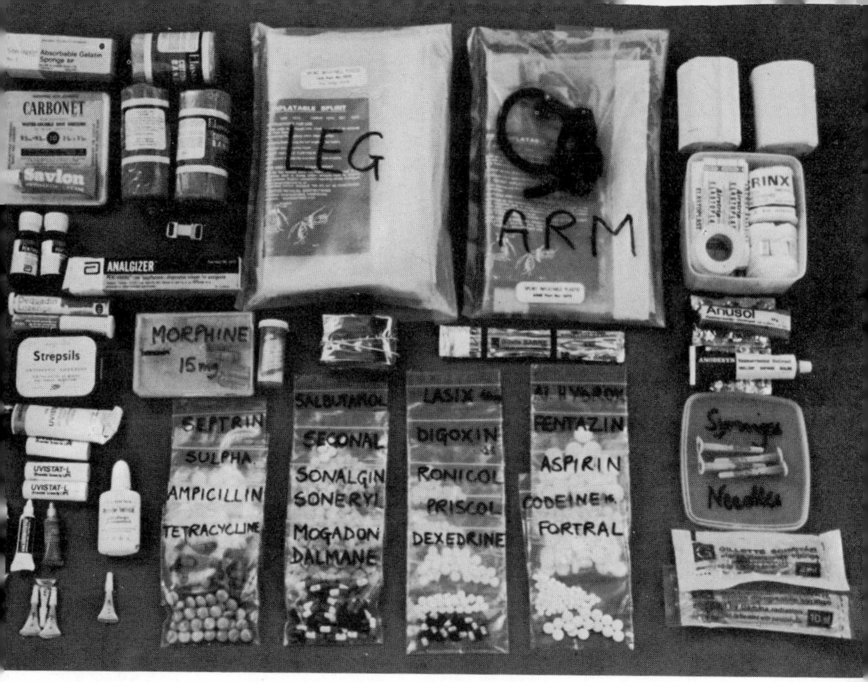

3. Medical kit supplied to the camp on the International Expedition. The packets marked 'Leg' and 'Arm' contain inflatable splints.

from camp. For forays away from base a similar box can be taken to tide the party over. If there is a doctor in the party he will carry his own comprehensive bag and a resuscitation kit as well. The contents will be entirely decided by the personal preference of the doctor and his degree of experience. If he has never done a tracheotomy or given an anaesthetic before, he is wise not to start learning in a two-man tent 20,000 ft up in a blizzard.

Editors' note. Rather than print a pharmacopoeia we refer you to Peter Steele's book, *Medical Care for Mountain Climbers*, published by Heinemann Medical Books 1976. As many of the drugs are not available without prescription and your medical needs will vary according to the size and location of your expedition, you will have to consult your doctor or medical officer when organizing your supplies. *JB-S and AB*

3. JUNGLE EXPLORATION
by John Blashford-Snell

The very word jungle gives rise to a feeling of excitement. But in some it also causes a feeling of fear; a claustrophobic fear of that dark, impenetrable vegetation in which lurk great beasts and hostile natives! However in reality it is not as bad as you may imagine and indeed the 'jungle is neutral'. It can be a friend or an enemy and the whole matter of living and moving in this strange terrain really comes down to an attitude of mind.

I define it as any uncultivated forest in the tropics, but there are many different forms of jungle including the hot wet tropical rain forest and the drier open scrub country.

Its composition is by no means constant, even in similar climatic zones, for the density and type of vegetation depends upon the altitude and also on the influence of man. The immensely tall tropical trees can take over 100 years to mature and usually are only found fully grown in virgin forest. This is called primary jungle and it is here that the great trees rise up to 70 metres and may measure more than 3 metres wide at the base. The topmost branches form a dense canopy over 35 metres from ground level and because little sunlight can penetrate, there is comparatively thin undergrowth on the jungle floor. As a result travel for men on foot is fairly easy in most areas of primary jungle and you will find many of the animals living in the high canopy. Where the primary forest has been burned and cleared for cultivation the jungle is quick to reclaim the area once man has retreated. The action of sunshine and heavy rain causes a tangled wilderness of plants and vegetation to grow up from the forest floor and this produces secondary jungle through which it can be very difficult to move. Visibility is often only a few metres and you have to cut a way.

The evergreen rain forest that forms a belt either side of the equator eventually becomes monsoon forest where conditions are slightly different. Here during the dry season many trees shed their leaves and the forest streams dry up. During this season moving through such areas (as are found in the *terai* of Nepal) is relatively easy and pleasant.

At high altitude another type is found called montane forest. This can be a colder clammy form of jungle that is nearly impenetrable. Masses of tangled roots, creepers and vegetation are covered in a grey slime to form a mat, sometimes 3 metres thick above the level of the ground. Movement under these conditions is both hellish and hazardous. Fortunately such forests are only found in a few areas.

Near the equator the noonday sun is usually almost vertically overhead and so there is little seasonal variation. In fact the main temperature difference occurs between day and night, especially on high ground where it can be extremely chilly after dark.

In general, whilst many areas of jungle look the same, the actual species of the fauna and flora are different. The local people are of different races, although they do have some similarities; and, contrary to expectation, they are generally friendly.

Before considering the organization of an expedition in jungle it is wise to think about the problems that man faces by himself. Many people have an entirely false impression of the risks and dangers involved. They imagine that large animals and snakes are the real hazards but although wild animals may be found they are usually frightened of man. In fact the greatest dangers lie in the cumulative effect of a number of factors which can be summarized as follows:

1. Panic, due to claustrophobia or when lost.
2. The effects of climate, and sickness originating from these.

3. Tropical diseases, especially those borne by insects.
4. The fear of animals.
5. Poisoning by contact with or by eating certain plants.

The best way to overcome panic is by knowledge of the difficulties you are likely to face.

When considering the hazards due to the climate naturally we think of the temperature. However, this is not always particularly high. In fact, it is humidity, combined with physical exertion, that makes you feel hot and causes heavy perspiration. This is why salt must be replaced and it is important to maintain your intake of water. The latter may even exceed $5\frac{1}{2}$ litres a day. Water is usually fairly easy to find in jungle areas but sometimes in the monsoon forest it may be more difficult. Vines may be cut with a machete to produce a steady supply of drinking water. But if this turns milky, don't drink it. Water from mountain streams is often safe but if there is any habitation nearby it should be boiled for at least ten minutes or treated with sterilizing tablets. A useful accessory, but not a substitute, is a Millbank Bag, which is issued to the British Army for filtering water. The effects of the sun and heat are highly dangerous and are frequently forgotten. Sunstroke, heatstroke or heat exhaustion are all illnesses of which you must beware. After a prolonged period under the jungle canopy you may suffer severe sunburn if you emerge into open grassland or even large clearings and during the crossing of the Darien Gap in 1972 many of us suffered in this way.

Insect-borne sicknesses can include malaria, dysentery, sandfly fever and typhus. Prevention is better than cure and simple precautions can often save days of agony. Malaria may be prevented by taking certain types of tablets and by avoiding mosquito bites. When mosquitoes are numerous it is advisable to keep the maximum amount of skin covered in spite of the discomfort; this is especially important at night, when of course you should sleep under a mosquito net. Dysentery is best prevented by avoiding unwashed local food, thoroughly cooking everything you eat and boiling all water. Hygiene plays an important part in the prevention of this distressing illness. To avoid sandfly fever simply avoid the sandfly! Although you cannot be injected against malaria, dysentery and sandfly fever, you can avoid typhus by inoculation and good personal hygiene. Similarly in many areas today there is a risk of cholera against which you can be vaccinated. I could go on writing about tropical diseases for a very long time, having suffered from several myself, but I strongly recommend that before entering a jungle area you should spend a little time studying the essentials of prevention and treatment of the more common diseases, and remember that a great deal of suffering can be avoided by simple precautions such as inoculation and personal hygiene.

The dangers from various forms of animal life vary throughout the world, but undoubtedly insects are high on the list. I have already mentioned the mosquito and I can only emphasize the importance of using nets and covering up. If you have not got a mosquito net, you must cover your body at night. If you can put up with the smoke it may help to sleep to leeward of a fire. Where possible, you should avoid swampy areas as these are where the mosquito breeds. Remember too that vampire bats also attack humans; they usually bite the toes—I know!

Bees, hornets and wasps are dangerous and their nests are easily recognized, looking like grey oblong masses on tree-trunks or branches. If you are unfortunate enough to disturb the inhabitants you can be subjected to the most vicious attack. But I have found that if you are a few metres away when the brutes emerge you can avoid being stung by keeping very still for about five or ten minutes then creeping silently away. Although they will chase you if you run, you can avoid them to some extent by dashing through the thickest undergrowth you can find!

Whilst leading an ill tempered stallion, appropriately named Randy, through the Darien Gap, the stupid beast decided to bite a hornets' nest. So I know all about being chased and stung!

Never try to pull off a leech or a tick as this will only leave the jaws in the bite to fester and irritate. The best way to remove them is with a touch of salt, tobacco or even the end of a lighted cigarette. At night it is usually wise for two of you to do a complete body check of each other, notwithstanding the complications that may arise with mixed-sex expeditions! It is amazing what you will find that has crept on to you during the day and you should pay particular attention to areas of body hair. In the Darien Gap I found forty-five ticks on my signaller's body and thought we had a record until he found fifty-six on me, but then I'm a large target.

Ants, spiders, scorpions and centipedes are all common in the tropics and may cause painful bites. They are often found in the bark of dead trees or under rocks. You should shake out your clothing and boots before dressing and remember to inspect the inside of sleeping bags, rucksacks and other cool shady containers before putting your hand in. In Zaïre I received an extremely painful scorpion sting whilst searching around for clean socks in a darkened pack. Only a whole tin of Waspeze numbed the hand!

Although there are over 2,000 known species of snakes, only 200 or so are poisonous. Very few will attack, but some defend their eggs or young to the death. Although it is not unusual to hear stories of natives who die of snake bite it is by no means a common occurrence and in twenty years of exploration I have only seen one person actually bitten by a snake; and in fact that was not poisonous. Snakes can feel the vibrations of your footsteps and will usually get out of your way. However, certain types, such as the rather heavy fatter varieties of vipers, are more dangerous because they are less likely to move and therefore there is a chance you will tread on them.

The pit-vipers locate their prey through heat-sensitive glands or pits on the side of the face. These snakes are found in jungle areas, especially in Central and South America. They may appear to come towards you whilst they are trying to sum up your heat pattern. Usually, having decided that you are too big a target, they will go away. But occasionally they can strike and one should beware of them when moving along jungle trails. In South America one of our officers suddenly looked up the trail to see a 10-foot bushmaster wobbling towards him. He drew his .45 Smith and Wesson, fired six shots at the snake, all of which missed, so hurled the revolver at it and ran. A few days later our reconnaissance team leader, Captain David Bromhead of the Royal Regiment of Wales, had to shoot off a bushmaster's head after it had embedded its teeth in the rubber heel of his jungle boot and would not let go! The next week Sgt Partapsing Limbu, our Gurkha NCO, turned just in time to find one of these unpleasant reptiles bearing down on him; he beheaded it with his razor-sharp Kukri.

Water and sea snakes are often less poisonous, but may be avoided by bombarding your selected bathing or crossing point with rocks before entering the water.

In spite of sensational stories, constrictors such as the python or boa do not attack humans. Many of these large snakes are aquatic and are often found near streams. If you are really hungry they are quite good to eat. Try cutting off the head, peeling away the skin and roast the resulting snake steaks—it tastes like rubbery chicken! But as a general rule unless you are attempting to collect snakes and know something about what you are doing, my advice is to avoid them all.

Other reptiles that may be dangerous include alligators, caiman and crocodiles. They are found in or around streams and lakes but can travel quite long distances over land. Although they will usually try to get away from you it is possible that if you are in between one and the water it may strike at you with its lashing tail as it passes! Large stones thrown into likely places will usually scare them off but they can be very hard to see and at times have been known to keep extremely still and lie low until you are right on top of them.

I remember an incident that occurred early one morning on an Ethiopian lake, that I described in my earlier book:

'It was barely light when we left the camp and coming to the water's edge we decided to walk out along a partly finished jetty, to get a good view. I led the way followed by Negussie and then Bill. We all had our arms filled with oddments of reconnaissance kit and made our way forward by hopping from the top of one timber pile to the next, never more than a couple of feet above the water. Almost at the end of the jetty I looked down and saw what I thought was a large, rubber tyre, with the tread just on the surface of the water.

' "Is that a tyre or could it be a crocodile?" I asked Negussie. As if to answer he used a red-and-white striped surveyor's pole he was carrying to press firmly down in the centre of the object. It sank without movement, and as he released the pole, bobbed up again.

' "Ah, obviously a tyre," we all thought and took another pace forward. At that moment, Negussie repeated the process but this time the result was different. With a great roar and a crash a leviathan rose up from the depths. It was a large crocodile and its tail came crashing round to strike the timbers just beneath my feet, sending splinters flying in all directions. At the same time it launched itself at Negussie, who fortunately being extremely agile, leapt to the top of a convenient pile. The beast then turned on me and with his mouth wide open displaying serried lines of yellowing teeth, tried to get my leg. In one hand I held a .303 sporting rifle and in the other I carried more survey equipment. Flicking the safety catch off with my thumb, I thrust my rifle down into the gaping mouth and pulled the trigger. The jaws closed about the barrel as the gun went off. Blood spurted out towards me, and at that moment Bill and Negussie fired their weapons into it. With an awful gurgling sound, it began to slide back into the water.

' "Hold it, quickly," yelled Negussie, and before we could stop him, had seized the thing by the tail. It took us nearly an hour to get the carcass of the reptile ashore and finally we carried it back to camp in triumph in a Land-Rover. It was a salutary lesson and one I'm not likely to forget. It brings out the old maxim that the crocodile will very often attack after you have stepped over him and not when you are about to. Frankly it was as close as I want to get to one.'[1]

Most doctors will agree that amateur attempts at using snake bite kits, cutting around the wound with razor blades or rubbing in various crystals are dangerous. My advice on simple immediate first aid is to treat for shock, try to catch and kill the snake that has caused the bite so that it may be identified to help decide which serum should be used for treatment and keep the patient still, until a doctor can be found. I've also been told that the affected limb should be kept below the level of the heart.

It is very unusual for a large animal to attack without any provocation. However, I have been charged by elephant and once a lioness and her cubs jumped straight over me! Wounded animals or aged ones which are no longer able to hunt for themselves can be dangerous and buffalo or wild pig have been known to charge in thick forest. If you consider that there is a serious risk in the area you will need a very heavy rifle if you are to defend yourself adequately against the larger animals. Nevertheless, I have found that by making a fair amount of noise, keeping a fire going at night, or urinating on the track either side of your camp, you will usually keep large game away. Naturally if you block a hippo's exit from a river at the only place where it can climb up a steep bank you may expect trouble. Likewise if you camp beside a water hole you can expect to see a large number of animals.

Game trails may be the only tracks available to you. Indeed, in most little-explored jungle areas roads and air strips are few and it is usually the rivers and lakes that provide the best routes. Cutting tracks through jungle is a long and arduous business, and you cannot expect to advance at anything more than a mile per hour at the most. If your expedition is prolonged you will

[1] *Where the Trails Run Out*, Hutchinson, 1974.

also have the problem of keeping the trails open, for vegetation grows extremely quickly and disused tracks can be covered in secondary growth within a matter of months.

As far as poisonous plants are concerned I recommend a local botanist should be consulted.

It is unlikely that you will be able to travel in a compass line directly through the jungle. I have found that one's choice of routes is normally restricted to streams, rivers, dry waterways, game trails, native paths and along the crests of ridges. These jungle routes all tend to run parallel to or to follow the tilt of the land. Few tracks will cross from one valley to another or traverse a series of crests; instead they tend to run down the valleys or along the intervening ridges. If you can find a suitable path, even if it is up to 30° off your required direction, I suggest it is better to use it than no track at all. Map reading in the jungle is not easy, however, and for goodness sake trust your compass because jungle trails tend to meander as do the rivers. If you are lost and want a village you will find that most tracks will eventually lead you to one; following rivers can be a way of reaching civilization but it can also extend your journey considerably.

It is quite easy to get lost in the jungle and I would suggest that if you are not familiar with the route and want to return to your base later you should slash or 'blaze' trees to show the white under-bark or you should cut leaves and turn them upside down. Pieces of material or paper can also be used to mark a route. To attract attention you will find that by banging the trunk of a tall tree with a stick you make a drumming noise which carries a good distance. I recommend that you avoid rushing blindly forward and if you are in a large party send a scout or reconnaissance team ahead of you. One way for a group to move is to have a cutter at the front who is changed over from time to time when he becomes tired. But remember that you hit decaying vegetation or a rotten tree at your peril—it can easily fall on top of you! Large decayed trees frequently collapse by themselves, so if camping for the night it is best not to sleep beneath them. In gulleys and ravines you may find a mass of boulders and tree roots which are covered with mould and moss that has formed a false layer. It is easy to fall through this and injure yourself. Beware!

You can navigate, even if you have no compass, by the direction of the sun, although at midday when it is directly overhead this may be difficult.

Streams may be crossed with rafts of bamboo or other lightweight wood, but avoid hard woods as these do not float. I once spent three hours building a superb raft, but it sank as soon as I stood on it!

On the march in the jungle it is best to stop about once every hour to clean insects, ticks and other creepy crawlies off and you will find that because the sun goes down very early it is wise to stop in mid-afternoon to make camp while you can still see. Before setting up your camp you should clear away all dead leaves and vegetation from beneath your sleeping area. This will lessen the chance of insects and snakes disturbing you during the night.

Naturally you must sleep above the ground and a hammock is the best answer. If you have not got one, then make yourself a bed above ground level. Your mosquito net should be hung above this and finally top the whole thing off with some sort of waterproof protection, ideally a ground sheet, although you can also use large leaves or some sort of thatch. Remember that ravines and river beds may flood when a storm occurs on nearby or even distant high ground. If you are going to remain in the area for anything more than a few hours your ablutions and latrines must be well away from the camp to avoid attracting flies and they must also be sited where they will not contaminate the water you propose to drink. So don't camp immediately downstream from a village.

To get a fire going I suggest you pick a spot where it is unlikely to spread but is still as dry and as sheltered as possible. You should collect a plentiful supply of firewood before actually starting the fire. However, be careful with bamboo as it contains air-filled cavities which can explode with some violence, hurling flaming splinters in all directions. If you must use bamboo, use your machete to open up these cavities.

Matches are a vital part of any survival kit you may carry, but remember you can still light fires with improvised flints, magnifying glasses or even two pieces of wood.

If your rations run out and you have no cooking utensils you can live very well off the land. The jungle is a living larder and I recommend that you read a book on survival before entering the forest. Fish, small animals, snakes and even insects are all edible. Local fruit is usually fairly easy to obtain and cooking can be done with the aid of lengths of bamboo. Your body needs salt if it is to continue functioning properly and therefore you should always carry some with you. In an emergency it can be obtained from certain plants, or dissolved out of sea water. If fresh water is difficult to obtain in any quantity you may be able to get some if you are near the sea. By digging down a few feet above high water level you should find water will soon collect. Stop digging then and test to see if it is free from salt, which it should be. This is because the fresh water floats on top of the salt water and therefore you should not dig too deeply. You could find that it tastes slightly brackish but it is usually safe to drink. If you really are in trouble you may be able to get help from the local people. I have found that jungle dwellers are usually friendly even if somewhat timid, and you need to be patient with them. The best advice I can give is that you show no fear and offer them small gifts. Salt is especially appreciated and nowadays many of them understand that pills, even aspirins, have their uses. Should you have taken the trouble to learn something of the local language before entering the area you will find that it pays enormous dividends. At one time I thought I was pretty good at Arabic and was trying to assist our expedition doctor to save the life of an ailing baby. The Arab mother was one of the Mudir's concubines and naturally I was only permitted to converse with

4. John Blashford-Snell with an Indian who had not previously seen a white man, on the Darien Gap Expedition of 1972.

her through a curtain. It was with considerable difficulty that I tried to translate the doctor's medical questions and her answers. All the village men had gathered to watch this performance. Suddenly a great cheer went up and I later discovered to my horror that I had asked her to marry me.

If you are going to plan an 'expedition' in jungle then the very name suggests this is something requiring organization. I believe there are a number of factors to consider including the reason for going in the first place. It may be that there is a scientific or medical quest, or even a search for a little-known people or a lost city. I think it is unlikely that you will be going in there just to prove yourself.

'Time spent on reconnaissance is seldom wasted' and if you are unable to visit the region before your expedition I strongly suggest that you make a study of the best maps available. Nowadays much of the world has been photographed from satellites as part of the NASA programme. This material may be purchased at a reasonable cost from EROS Data Center, Sioux Falls, SD 57198, USA. At the time of writing there are also copies available for inspection at the Science Reference Library (Bayswater), 10 Porchester Gardens, London W2 4DL.

Side-Looking Airborne Radar (SLAR) is a type of remote sensing technique which is being increasingly used for making images of those parts of the world usually covered with heavy cloud. This type of imagery is essentially orthographic and is very useful for simple navigation and various scientific purposes.

If you can obtain ordinary air photographs these too are very useful but of course you must beware of attracting suspicion if you walk around in a developing country carrying masses of maps and aerial photographs, particularly if they have any military markings or origins.

As a result of the preliminary study of your area you should be able to make an appreciation of the best way of conducting your expedition in this particular terrain. Undoubtedly you will find yourself trying to decide on the best route. It may be that it is most suitable for your expedition to move by river with supplies coming in overland. However, you might equally well decide to move overland and bring your supplies in by river. On the other hand, if you are fortunate enough to have some air support then you can use parachute resupply, using parachutes fitted with long 'jungle lines', to keep you going.

If you decide to use the rivers as your main route then you will have to decide which craft is most suitable. Hovercraft have the advantage that they can go upstream against the current. But small hovercraft will only carry a limited amount of stores and of course you may have mechanical difficulties, although recent advances in their development have overcome these to a large degree; and there is still the problem of getting fuel.

If you are content to have a one-way journey (i.e. downstream), then a canoe or an inflatable boat may be the answer. Canoes can easily be managed by one man and are an inexpensive way to travel. However, they can only carry a limited amount of equipment and are not quite so simple to transport in aircraft as inflatable boats.

Inflatable craft of a reputable make, such as those produced by the Avon Rubber Company, are extremely tough and remarkably stable. They do not puncture easily and indeed I have only ever seen one inflatable punctured accidentally in a buoyancy tube on an expedition. Their light weight and buoyancy make them extremely safe and easy to move about. They can carry heavy loads and will negotiate fearsome white water. They can be folded up, carried in small aircraft and even parachuted. The Services have been using inflatables for years and Avons are now almost standard equipment on most big expeditions from the Polar Regions to the Equator.

On the Zaïre River Expedition giant inflatables reaching approximately 40 feet were used with incredible success and it is likely that these will be available on the market by the time this book is in print. These huge craft could carry up to 20 tons in emergencies. Nevertheless, inflatables are not always the answer because when fully loaded, they move slowly and their width makes it difficult to use them in narrow waterways. There is one other slight disadvantage that we discovered on the Zaïre River. Hippos don't like inflatable boats and one took several large bites out of an Avon. The result was five very frightened men (including an Army Chaplain who thought he was on his way to Head Office), one very useless boat and one hippo with a disastrous attack of wind!

Local boats, particularly dugout canoes, powered very often by small outboard motors and handled skilfully by natives, are a good way to travel if you do not want to use your own craft. Such boats can often go upstream against quite fierce currents and the boatmen are usually experts. However, it does cost money to hire them and you always have the problem of fuel.

Undoubtedly the finest upstream craft is the jetboat. These highly manoeuvrable shallow draught craft are still a relatively new type of transport but already they have proved themselves on rivers throughout the world. However, they are not quite so simple to handle as you might think and they are both expensive to buy and to run. They cannot be portaged without considerable difficulty and they are noisy. Nevertheless, if you must go upstream against a raging river there is no boat available at present that will manage it other than a jet.

For your overland movement you have a wide choice of animals and vehicles. In general the animals are more reliable. There are mules which are sturdy, horses which are not and elephants which carry enormous loads. Donkeys, camels and yaks may also be used where they are available. Of the equine beasts, my own choice would be a mule. Nevertheless, horses did brilliantly during the crossing of the Darien Gap and in spite of all forebodings twenty-three out of the twenty-eight horses survived. However, there were some difficulties as my log for that expedition recalls:

'The Pathfinder is now five miles south of the Meteti and going well. Ernie has now joined it. Unfortunately he has lost Cromwell [my bay horse], who was nearly driven mad by the blood-suckers and vampires. Corporal Yuen [of the Royal Engineers] dressed him in a length of parachute silk in the form of a nightdress, as a protection after dark. One night he escaped and rampaged through several Indian villages, a pink apparition, causing great consternation, especially when he passed through a drinking orgy.'

Contrary to common belief, horses can feed off the jungle providing you can supply them with some additional roughage and in the Darien Gap this was done by air-dropping quantities of sweet corn to them. Donkeys are probably better in desert conditions than in the jungle but although I have used them with success they cannot carry a very great load. I have yet to see camels and yaks used in forests, although I am told this has been done. More recently I have been involved with Indian elephants and am full of praise for these dignified creatures. To the best of my knowledge there are no working elephants in Africa now, although there were some in Zaïre, but the Indian elephant has long been domesticated and appears to be very simple to feed, look after and will go on reliably under adverse conditions in forests with very little trouble. With the possible exception of the equine animals, I believe that you may need to hire local handlers to come with you and look after the livestock.

As regards vehicles, it takes a great deal to beat the faithful Land-Rover, but Jeeps and Toyota Land-Cruisers and many other makes have been used with success. In jungle there are often ravines which make perfect vehicle obstacles and thus you will need to build bridges. To some extent this may be overcome by the use of specially made lightweight aluminium ladders, reaching up to 14 feet in length which can be carried on the vehicle roof.

To wade, the vehicles must be equipped with some sort of snorkel and to cross the bigger rivers a raft may be necessary. This could be an inflatable or rigid structure and in the Darien two Avon M650 boats were used with great success for this purpose. They had the advantage of being able to be packed up and stowed in the back of a Range-Rover and when the time came could be inflated and used to float the vehicle across a river.

In general, tracked vehicles are better in muddy conditions than wheeled. However, these are often much more expensive and difficult to maintain. Under hot conditions it is also possible that the mud can ooze into the tracks and then set like concrete, gluing the vehicle up very successfully. This happened to us in the jungles of Panama and we had to abandon two small tracked carriers as a result.

Motorcycles and bicycles have also been used in tropical forests, although personally I think there are easier ways of moving.

You should not forget man himself as a means of transport and in many tropical areas it is possible to obtain porters. However, you should not assume that you will always be able to find them, for there are certain people who regard it beneath their pride to carry heavy goods. In Nepal the Sherpas are extremely well organized and I have found the Indians in South America most helpful. My only advice here is that you should appoint a Sirdar or head man to watch over the column and deal entirely through him. It is best not to pay them all the money in advance and to keep a careful eye on the number of loads as you go along.

For your air support you will have an enormous range of aircraft but on many expeditions I have used a British Army Air Corps Beaver, which is made by the De Havilland Company in Canada. These aircraft are truly the Land-Rovers of the air, and can be fitted with floats if necessary to land on rivers. Good pilots and regular maintenance are essential for jungle expeditions. Diversionary airfields are few and far between and your chances of survival if you crash in the trees are not high. I recommend that all aircraft used to support jungle expeditions should at least be painted some fluorescent colour. If you intend to drop stores by parachute through the jungle canopy, then special jungle lines will have to be attached to the load to prevent it becoming snagged in the top of the trees.

Autogiros are an interesting idea although I have never tried them, but helicopters, although ideal, are very expensive to run. They need a great deal of maintenance and have a limited range. Because of their vertical take off and landing ability, we may see airships being used to support jungle expeditions in future. I am told that at present one of the limiting factors is the need for stocks of the inert helium gas in the areas over which they might operate, although they can still use hydrogen, which is cheaper and easier to obtain. There is also certain doubt as to how they will perform in tropical storms. I have a feeling that the days of the airship are not over and if used during windless periods (i.e. early morning) they could provide extremely valuable aerial platforms for reconnaissance.

Now we come to the question of equipment.

For your own clothing I recommend good-quality, loose-fitting cotton for working garments. Army uniform made of pale khaki or green drill is ideal. Insects seem to be attracted to the brighter colours and also, by the way, to strong perfume! Shirts should have long sleeves and be capable of being fastened at the wrists. It is better for the trousers to be long and capable of being fixed inside jungle boots as a protection against insects. Ideally the best boot for jungle is the US Army style Tropical Combat Boot, available on the civilian market in USA. However, hockey or baseball type rubber boots are also suitable. I believe that you should wear a lightweight broad-brimmed hat which will give protection against falling insects and quite naturally I recommend the British pith helmet as being supreme!

Rucksacks may have frames or not, according to your choice, but if you are based on boats I believe it is better not to have a frame as this is easily damaged. By choice I carry one of the larger Berghauz variety which is wonderfully waterproof with lots of useful pockets and broad carrying straps. Naturally you should carry a reliable compass (a Silva type has a mirror which is useful for shaving and signalling), a waterproof map, a machete, your sleeping equipment, changes of clothing, possibly some spare boots and a survival kit which is actually on your person and not in the pack. Water-bottles are essential and should be carried on the waist. I believe that a belt kit is a good idea and all the really vital things are there so that if the boat turns over or the mule bolts or the porters flee and your pack is lost, you can still survive. Remember to take some files or stones for sharpening your machete and you may need some flares for attracting aircraft. The jungle is not full of animals waiting to attack you and so it is unlikely that you will need a firearm but if you do I recommend a shotgun as being one of the most useful to have for general purpose work. You can get a variety of cartridges for it and at close range it will stop most animals in their tracks. However, if you feel that you must carry a hand gun then I suggest a good quality revolver of at least .357 inch calibre (such as a Smith and Wesson or a Colt). Remember, a revolver is rather like a lifeboat hanging down the side of the ship—it is of no use whatsoever unless you know how to use it and it will function when required! For this reason I don't like automatic pistols that are prone to jam under muddy or sandy conditions.

Engineer equipment such as power saws, carabiners and cordage may well be necessary for pioneer work. Fishing equipment will help to keep you in fresh food and a few simple snares may even catch you some larger animals if you are starving. Waterproof binoculars, cameras in waterproof cases, waterproof notebooks and preservative for your equipment are other items you may need. If you have anything made of leather it will go mouldy unless you make regular applications of Neatsfoot oil. I find a lightweight anorak is useful for when the monsoon rain is pelting down. Finally, try out all your equipment before setting out and give it a really thorough testing. I have placed great emphasis on the word 'waterproof' because everything in the jungle is damp and plastic bags, aluminium containers and plastic containers are all invaluable.

Man has found that he can cross the Polar regions with tracked vehicles and dog sledges and he can motor over the desert in Land-Rovers. Swamps can be crossed by hovercraft and the sea is no barrier but we have yet to find a vehicle that will go with impunity through tropical forests. As a result it is the jungle areas of the world that are still the least known and the least explored. Nevertheless they are fast being eroded by the progress of mankind and I believe that it is very important to remember the need for the conservation of the fauna, the flora and the people of these remote regions.

4. DESERT AND BUSH EXPLORATION

by David Hall

Deserts have a strange fascination which has in the past caught many explorers and travellers. Burke and Wills, Doughty, Laing, Rholfs, Monod, Bagnold, and, perhaps the last of the great explorers, Thesiger, were all its victims to some degree. Those whom I have known on desert expeditions have either loved or hated it, and few have been anything but positive. This is synonymous with the harsh way of life of desert dwellers and bushmen. For many months of a year they live on the wrong side of the bread-line, most of them with a centuries-old background of tribal battles and loyalties, with an unprecedented generosity and understanding of friends, and with a religion befitting one of the harsher environments the earth can offer. The deserts and bush are uncompromising, and so too, I believe, are human attitudes towards them. After the hardness of the daytime heat and glare, I remember evenings when the dropping sun turned the desert into a paradise of calm, aglow with orange and yellow light, giving cool shadows, and producing an immense sense of wellbeing. Meanwhile the fire of dried roots and camel dung blazed under the small teapot producing the all important brew for traveller and guide. As the sun fell a new enemy crept over the desert: the bitter cold of night which was so often heralded by a rising wind, as though to blow through to chill the bones. Such extremes demand unusual methods of living and moving in deserts and bush.

In this chapter I shall discuss deserts almost to the exclusion of bush, for the latter covers a broad spectrum of terrain varying from different sorts of sub desert through to the bush of tropical coastal plains. The problems vary so much that I shall restrict my comments to the types of bush that are similar to deserts.

Deserts conjure up to many people shimmering sand dunes, and oases of refreshing sweet, blue water surrounded by vivid green palm trees. In fact, most comprise a mixture of broken plateaux, often depicted so beautifully in Jordan, vast sand seas as found in Algeria's Grand Erg Oriental, weird rock formations such as the high rock towers (aiguilles, or needles) of northern Tibesti, endless plains of gravel and dust as shown by the Calanscio Serir in Libya, and mountainous desert as found in the Atacama in Chile. Deserts arise from the interplay of land masses with oceanic currents and climatic patterns, and their surface and aridity make them some of the most difficult areas of the world for living and movement. The lack of features and frequently inadequate maps make desert travel resemble navigating oceans. Just as at sea, a compass course is set, and the distance is checked, so that at the end of the day the traveller knows where he should be on the earth's surface. He can verify his position by checking the angles of the stars against his exact time using simple tables. At sea the principles are exactly the same. One incident of early desert training with the Army drove home the likeness of desert to sea, when John Blashford-Snell was trying to raise funds for the Squadron to hire camels. He only got money when he appealed to the Royal Naval staff, persuading them that he needed money to hire ships, 'ships of the desert'. The camels were hired.

The aridity also makes deserts strangely timeless which is one of the main attractions to research. While doing a very general survey of small parts of the Hamada el Akdamin in south-eastern Libya, an expedition from the Royal Military Academy, Sandhurst found some Neolithic sites on the terraces of wadis, or ancient water courses. Without doubt they were walking up wadis which no European had seen; and along one, with particularly steep sides and a winding water course, footsteps were almost hushed as though in a cathedral, for there was an uncanny feeling that a Neolithic family might be round the next corner sheltering from the hot sun beneath one of the sandstone overhangs. The family never materialized, but the landscape can have changed little since those earlier days, though it was damper then, with sufficient grass to maintain the animals whose tracks, fossilized in the black 'desert varnish', were so clear. This sense of timelessness probably comes about by the relative lack of interference by humans. In most deserts thousands of years have passed since the climate allowed vegetation on the right scale to support more than a nomadic population. The land has not been developed by farmers or builders, so the Neolithic hearths and meal stores of bones remain untouched just below the surface, and implements of that and earlier ages lie where they were left on the desert's surface many millennia before. The soils, too, are those of the past, having undergone no appreciable decay since then. Hence deserts provide an extremely useful ground for research into the earth's history, but the hostility of the land and its climate make it impossible to carry out that research without first preparing an expedition to be able to arrive and live in the desert. One must either rely on animal transport, or base one's life on mechanical vehicles.

Travel and support by camel is far easier to organize than motor transport. Camels do not break down, there is no need to carry spare parts, and at least if they die their meat and body fluids can be of use. They can get where motor transport cannot, and they can tolerate much rougher countryside than cars. However, they are slow, and their payload is limited to a few hundred pounds. The 1970 Aïr Mountains Expedition was saved by camels from a wasted two weeks when, having crossed the Sahara, one party of three Land-Rovers, within sixty miles of its objective, had only one serviceable vehicle left. It would have been foolish to proceed further into desert unknown to the team; so, returning to the second vehicle with a broken half shaft, they located a Tuareg family who had the only camels in the region, hired some beasts, and the archaeologists and geomorphologists were able to continue to the objective and get on with the work. Arranging camels is often difficult, and there are many stories of travellers waiting an age, and far from patiently, for their beasts to be brought in from pasture. Days pass with no sign of the long awaited animals, and the imagination shows the camel drivers slowly going about their business of collecting them together, but at the same time much enjoying the opportunity of drinking coffee or tea with all their friends in the region. It is a good chance for a splendid series of parties to catch up on all the desert gossip. Eventually the traveller sees the long awaited caravan appearing over the horizon, but even then he knows that the delays are not over, for there is saddlery to be borrowed and assembled, and the camels probably need watering. The pace of the desert is slow, and there is time for anything. So the authorities in oases can be alarmed and suspicious at the foreign traveller's need to hurry. I have enjoyed the days in an oasis firstly haggling and discussing terms over the traditional non-alcoholic brew. It is always satisfying then to see the camels which have been the subject of so much discussion. Perhaps they will look as though they would never carry half the required load, or perhaps they will come right up to expectation, giving confidence for the coming weeks. It is a great dividend to have those preliminary days in the oasis to strike up a relationship with the local people and with the guide and camel hands.

I found that arranging camels for a journey from the oasis of Mizda in Tripolitania in 1962 was particularly easy, and I quote from my diary:

'*26th December*. I arrived by the local bus at about ten in the evening. The oasis was dark, but the lights of the bus were sufficient for passengers and animals to disembark quickly; and for bags, sacks, suitcases and all manner of baggage and paraphernalia to be passed down from the roof. Hurried greetings and words of farewell and the noises of sorting baggage soon ended, and suddenly there were few people left round the bus. Before the driver disappeared I managed to discover from him that I should report to the old Italian Fort which housed the police. On arrival there I had my passport examined by the light of a paraffin lamp by a sleepy policeman. He seemed a kindly man so I explained that I had nowhere to sleep. He took me into the fort to a room with two bed frames with broken springs, and a chair, offering me one of the beds for the night.

'I awoke this morning to find a Tuareg in the bed next to mine. He was a mysterious person who seemed extremely suspicious when I greeted him in his own language.

'After breakfast of bread and sultanas I set off to organize camels, and almost at once had a volunteer, Ahamed bin Dau, an elderly man who looked hardly strong enough for the journey. It all took me many hours of bargaining, which was done in a local coffee shop often to an audience of up to twenty interested Arabs. Eventually we agreed upon two camels and Ahamed for the ten day journey for £15. He and I then set off to buy supplies for the journey . . . Poor fellow [Ahamed] seems rather uncertain about our journey. However, I'm sure he will turn out well.

'*27th December* . . . The camels arrived on time, Ahamed's beast carrying two tin water barrels. The other camel looked strong, and onto this we loaded all the other stores in two large saddle-bags of woven camel hair and wool. I had bought a small camel bag for carrying what I needed during the day. How wonderful it was to be mounted on a camel again in the open desert . . . . I note that we drive the camels from behind, beating them into a walking pace rather than leading them. When mounted, and steering the camel from its back, unlike the Tuareg system of holding the nose rope out to the side of the direction required, here we hold the stick out to the side of the head opposite to the proposed direction, and tapping the head if necessary, so forcing it over. We watered the camels and then ourselves at Bir Fesano, but the water was not very nice. We then walked on to an area of dunes for the night and there we met an Arab who had walked from Brak over 400 km away. He gave us dates mixed with a good deal of camel dung.'

When people ask what it is like to ride a camel, the reply is that, like riding a horse, it takes a good few days to get used to it. At first there is the inevitable soreness of the bones in the crotch and discomfort in the way one sits. My habit when travelling by camel is to walk during much of the day, perhaps only riding for one hour in three, and then normally at the end of the morning and afternoon. If time allows this much walking, which is slower, the camels will appreciate it! Far more of the desert's surface is seen from on high, but it takes too much time and effort to dismount to examine things such as implements and plants. I was thankful once to find myself on the camel's back while doing a compass survey of an escarpment in Tripolitania. Ahamed bin Dau, my guide, and I were riding peacefully across stony desert, when I saw, too late to change course, a horned viper exactly where I would have been walking.

On these journeys I found that the best clothes were a shirt, a warm pullover of thick white wool which always fascinated the Bedouin, a pair of baggy pantaloons and single-thonged sandals of the type worn by Tuareg, but I never bothered about a hat. The sandals are important, for boots or shoes get hot, sweaty and dusty, quickly causing blisters. This flip-flop type of sandal can be slipped on and off quickly and easily, simplifying the process of mounting and dismounting. Camels usually object to riders wearing boots, and in any case the toes help to control the beast when riding Tuareg fashion. Naturally, again for the camel's convenience, all luggage should if possible be in rounded soft containers. Suitcases are particularly unsuitable for any sort of desert travel as they either get dented or their hard corners tear other things. A bergan can be packed easily, and its metal frame placed away from the camel's back. It also provides a useful carrying frame for emergencies such as the loss of camels. It was some days after seeing the horned viper with Ahamed bin Dau that an emergency arose. Having stopped early in the evening in an area where there was a little pasture to be gleaned, Ahamed hobbled the camels loosely to allow them to wander with some freedom. At about ten that evening after we had eaten our usual macaroni and drunk our customary three glasses of strong, sweet tea, we went to find the camels to tether them safely for the night. We searched the wide, shallow valley of our own camp without success, and then the next one. At times we thought we had picked up their tracks with the aid of the torch, but each time we lost them. The moon was dropping and it became increasingly difficult to see so that eventually we were forced to give up and go to bed. That night I was thankful to have a bergan, but I waited until morning to work out how much we would have to carry in it. The following morning while despondently drinking our tea I luckily noticed three dots moving on a hill about five kilometres back along our route. It was the camels, so I was relieved that I did not have to resort to the use of the bergan for carrying water and food.

The camel is well known for its ability to endure long periods without water. Wilfred Thesiger, in his *Arabian Sands*, quotes a conversation in which he asks how long a camel will last in the summer. The Arab replied:

'Again it depends on the grazing. They will last longer in the wadis where they can get some shade from the trees. Under those conditions they would go for a week without a drink. In the sands we try to water them every two or three days.'[1]

The speed of the camel can be estimated quite accurately. A casual walking pace is about 3½ km per hour, though I recollect afternoons when the camels seemed to search every inch of desert for the faintest sign of a piece of dried scrub. Then I would estimate speeds of less than 2½ km per hour. When mounted and going well I have estimated speeds between 4½ and 7 km per hour. Well bred camels can trot for long periods and travel much faster. Dr Martin Williams and a colleague, each sitting on a camel behind a Tuareg, did 60 km in five hours, breaking the journey at midday to collect two sackloads of heavy fossil bones

[1]Longmans 1959.

from Taferjit. They found the journey extremely uncomfortable, especially as they had no saddles. The camels must have been especially strong and fit to carry two people each, and a sack of bones for the second half of the journey.

I once tried loading a camel, but soon learnt that it was best left to the guide. I was not too worried by all the barking, groaning and baring of teeth at me; but the load could not have been properly secured, for within a few minutes of starting it had slipped, much to the guide's disgust. Generally, however, camels are placid beasts. When once riding a bull camel I found it difficult to hold him back for about 17 km, and my guide explained that the poor animal could smell its opposite sex ahead. He was right enough, and getting my camel to move on from the herd of, no doubt, attractive young lady camels was a considerable task. I thought he had recovered from his anger at not being allowed to stay, and it was nearly a day later that he showed a final outburst of rage. Without warning my bull shot forward and bit my guide's camel hard on the backside. At this, guide and camel seemed to shoot into the air, but miraculously he landed safely in the saddle. That bite on his opponent's bottom was the only time I have seen a camel being really vicious. Like all other beasts, they vary a good deal, and the guide or camel hand will know their idiosyncrasies, and will also know how much each can reasonably carry. Most can manage a load of 100 kg, though none will of course admit it from the groaning that takes place during loading.

Navigation by camel is a simple matter of estimating speed and setting the course by prismatic compass, or by using a guide. A good guide with whom there is a common language is invaluable. He knows the land, the people, and can often help by naming plants, animals, insects, and also places. Mr W. B. Kennedy Shaw warned me that a reliable means of communication is essential. He told me of a desert traveller and surveyor in the Sudan who asked his guide the name of a hill he had just mapped. The guide replied that it was 'Ma-arifismo',

5. Caravan ready to move off.

and that name went onto the map. Translated it means: 'I don't know'.

Camels, then, are useful beasts of burden, and so long as there is a guide or camel hand, they are easily looked after. However, they are too slow for many expeditions, and a faster means of transport is often essential.

The twentieth century saw desert travel revolutionized by the petrol engine. Various types of car were tried in the desert in the hope of finding one suitable to the special conditions. Prince Kemal el Din with his half tracked motor cars was one of the earlier desert explorers to go by car. Brigadier Bagnold adapted the 'T' Type Ford, building his own car bodies onto the simple chassis. His ideas and developments became the basis for movement over the desert by the Long Range Desert Group in North Africa during the Second World War, and by desert travellers, expeditions, and exploration companies world-wide since.

The Land-Rover is now accepted almost universally as the most suitable vehicle for expeditions and travel over deserts. It is used by exploration companies who also, of course, have larger vehicles, as well as many of a specialized nature; but for overcoming obstacles the principles are the same. Deserts offer some interesting challenges to passage, each type of terrain presenting its own particular problems. The crossing of the smallest steep sided wadi can require momentum from the vehicle, grip from the tyres, and power from the engine. To achieve the necessary momentum with a heavily loaded truck over rough ground and up steep banks requires a strong chassis and sturdy suspension. The hardness of the suspension has to be balanced against the need to give the passengers a reasonably comfortable ride, for the juddering and shaking across uneven going can be unbearable on the nerves, particularly to those who do not have the steering wheel to make the choice of route. The way to help a vehicle over very rough ground is to drive slowly in the lowest possible gear, low ratio if necessary. It might be necessary for the passengers to dismount and help push the vehicle over obstacles, and at times even to winch, though this is rare.

Similar methods can be used for crossing soft sand, but there are extra and very necessary aids; and in the liquid soft sand that soon has a vehicle down to its axles it will not only be necessary to dismount the crew, but also sometimes to unload the heavy stores, carrying them to the next area of firm sand. However, that is the worst case, and with careful driving and good reconnaissance, soft sand of that nature is not often encountered. Driving over soft sand needs skill and experience as well as some simple equipment. The stability of the sand depends upon the packing of the grains, so that if the wind has moved the grains high and fast and they have been beaten to the ground, packing them into the smallest space, then the surface will withstand a good deal of pressure before breaking. Once the surface is broken, the careful sorting has been ruined, and the surface becomes softer. This destruction of the grain sorting can be achieved either by applying too much vehicle weight to too little tyre surface area, by skidding the wheels, by driving in another vehicle's tyre prints, or when stationary by walking in front of the motor car. The lessons from this are obvious. However, getting tyres with a larger surface area has to be assessed against the increased likelihood of these balloon-type tyres being damaged by sharp stones when driving over rocky desert. Whatever sort of tyre is chosen, it should have a smooth tread to avoid breaking the surface. A good compromise is the Michelin 'X', as it has fairly smooth surfaces and can be driven with the low pressures needed to give a large surface area in contact with the sand. When stretches of soft sand are known to exist it is good to plan the itinerary to face them in the early morning before the air gets warm and expands between the grains of sand, loosening their packing. In the early morning everyone is fresh, and if vehicles have to be dug out of soft sand, not too much water is lost in sweat. By the heat of midday the size of the job has increased enormously, so that tempers get short, and an awful lot of sweat is used, wasting water. The first time I crossed the north-west neck of the Edeyin Murzuq in the Fezzan was in the heat of the day. At one time all the vehicles were stuck deep to their axles, and we must have looked a pitiful and strange sight. The return journey, and every crossing thereafter, was done in the early morning with no fuss. It is surprising how much easier the second and subsequent crossings of difficult sand dunes are, and this is largely because drivers have confidence and know what to expect. Unless a reconnaissance has been made on foot over the dunes, feeling while walking for a firm route, the top of a dune might suddenly present to the unwary driver sand falling treacherously away at 34° for 40 metres or so, it might present a false crest with a nasty trough of soft sand, or it might give a smooth, firm run down into the next valley between the dune lines. These steep sided dunes have claimed a number of deaths from tumbling vehicles. I once drove into the dip from a very small steep sided dune in the southern Sahara, but luckily we were not heavily loaded, and neither vehicle nor occupants suffered more than a little shock. Air photographs show these steep sided dunes clearly, and are a useful aid to finding a way safely and quickly through a dune field so long as the driver's position can be found and followed on the photograph.

In the early days of desert motoring chicken wire was spread over the soft sand to help cars across, but it distorted easily and was not very effective. Then, almost by accident, a useful piece of equipment was found. Brigadier Bagnold had organized a small expedition to Petra, and Lieutenant Bader of the Royal Engineers set about finding some form of light portable ramps to take the cars up and down the small steep sided water channels they expected to find *en route*. He found in one old iron shop in the back streets of Cairo some rolled steel troughs used during the previous war for roofing bunkers. On that expedition they

6. Due to mechanical failures the Land-Rover had only front wheel drive and this, coupled with frequently soft sand, slowed progress. Digging out the vehicle entailed using four sand ladders in rotation, moving two metres at a time.

were in fact never once used, and lay about the mess garages until the next expedition when they were used for extricating cars from soft sand. They were five foot channels weighing about 15 kg, and, when placed in front of the back wheels, gave the vehicle a run to gain momentum, getting them out of the soft sand. The best drivers know when a vehicle is not going to fight its way out of soft sand, and they stop before skidding too much, breaking the careful packing of the grains. They have avoided the wretched situation of having to dig out the sand from chassis downwards. When stuck in soft sand the crew dig a gentle ramp in front of the back wheels and put the channels down so that they dig well back almost under the wheels. After clearing any sand in front of the front wheels, all hands push, and the vehicle edges forward onto the channels before thrusting with all speed up the ramps, with luck taking it onto firm sand beyond. It is important to dig out enough sand to prevent the channels sloping too steeply, for the torque imposed on the transmission is high under these conditions, and half shafts easily snap.

The south-western side of Libya is a lonely desert, and nobody much uses the route from el Gatrun down to the hills of Toummo on the border with Niger. Certainly when I took two Land-Rovers down across the broken plateau and sandy desert there were no signs of fresh tracks, and we therefore felt a long way from home when we broke a half shaft some twenty miles short of Toummo. We all piled onto one vehicle and limped 190 kilometres back to el Gatrun. On the way we were surprised to see one fresh set of tracks coming up from the direction of the Kourizo Pass and the Tibesti Mountains. This was most unusual since most travellers follow the rule of never travelling in single vehicles. Had we, for example, been in a single vehicle originally we would have had a long walk home. I later met the owner of the vehicle. While sitting on the doorstep of a resthouse in Agelhok in Mali on the western of the two main trans-Saharan routes, I was pointing out the names of a number of stars.

'You see the distant headlights coming from the north?

Directly above is Polaris, the North Pole Star, and it is this star which is so useful for assisting with direction-keeping at night.'

About twenty minutes later when the Land-Rover had arrived in the oasis, a small group shuffled towards us through the dark from the fort whose faint outline was just discernible. The Commandant, a small and friendly Tuareg was leading, and I reckoned that the visitor was the even smaller person with him.

'Mon Capitaine, nous avons une visiteuse. Peut-être voulez-vous traduire.'

The Long Wheel Base Land Rover Modified for Desert Travel

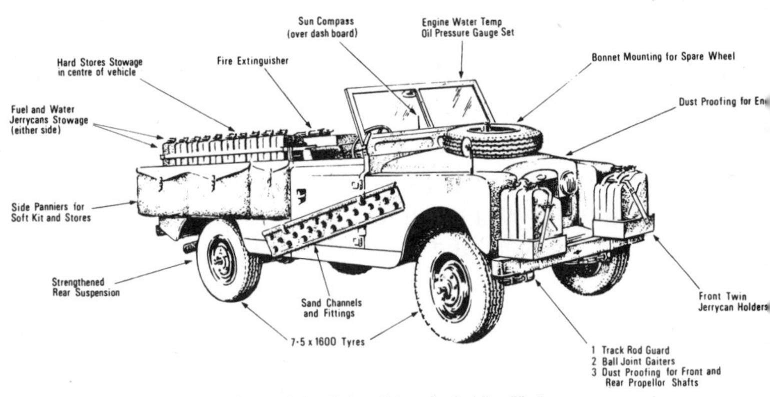

Note: Features indicated are those which the standard production vehicle requires for full modification

Drawing by Michael Saunders

I discovered to my delight that it was the traveller and writer, Barbara Toy, whom I had long wished to meet. Furthermore, I discovered that evening that they were her tracks north of Toummo. She too had broken a half shaft, but that had been many miles back in the Tibesti. She had travelled for about a week with one Tibu guide and neither of them spoke the other's language. It had been a rear half shaft, so she merely put the Land-Rover into four wheel drive, using the power on the front wheels to get her safely across one of the most dangerous stretches of desert.

Miss Toy's Land-Rover is prepared for world-wide travel,

with, now, a caravanette roof, giving her full protection from the weather. Some prefer open vehicles for desert travel, giving excellent all-round observation, easy access to the cargo, with nothing in the way of the sun so that the sun compass can be mounted between the driver and navigator. Furthermore, by lowering the windscreen onto the bonnet, the occupants really feel the cooling wind, and less dust is sucked back from the sometimes smokescreen-like plume following the vehicle across

7. An expedition loads up from its mud hut base. The canvas carriers outslung on either side are for carrying soft equipment and stores.

the desert. On the other hand there is a need to secure belongings in a closed Land-Rover in many desert oases these days. A useful vehicle layout has been developed over a series of expeditions, and involves building a metal framework which keeps jerrycans stored on the side benches in the back, and canvas panniers for soft stores outslung each side. Two further metal frames hold jerrycans to the front bumpers. This gives a total of twenty-two jerrycans held in the frames of a long wheel base Land-Rover, and provides plenty of space for boxes and tins in the main cargo space at the back. If further petrol or water is needed a forty-gallon drum can be placed on end just behind the front seats, but it is advisable to put it onto some stout wood to spread the load on the alloy floor.

Spare parts always present a problem. It is really a matter of working out the acceptable risks, otherwise there is a danger of taking two of everything, leaving no payload for anything else. What spares are taken depends on the condition of the vehicles, the availability of spares at the expedition's base, and how much weight and space can be allowed for them. Many expedition reports include recommended lists of spare parts to be carried, and these lists are one of the many things indexed in the Royal Geographical Society's unique collection of about four hundred expedition reports.

Navigating across deserts is challenging, and, if correctly done, it is immensely satisfying. If a guide is hired as the prime means of navigating, care must be taken to ensure that he has experience of travelling by car, and not only by camel. If he knows only animal transport, he will tend to follow routes across country suitable to them and not necessarily to cars; and he will be in danger of losing his bearings when travelling at a speed so much faster than he is used to. I was once asked to carry another party's guide back to Iferouane from Adrar Bous in Niger. He was an elderly man, brother of an old friend, Azowi; but this was a famous guide from times of French rule. I knew the route well, and in any case always checked by using the sun compass for direction and the milometer for distance. After about twenty miles Azowi's brother tried to persuade me to go further to the right, but I stuck to my guns. He continued trying to give me directions for about ten minutes, but then resigned himself to allowing this mad foreigner to have his own way. That evening we were relieved that we had not heeded his advice, for we discovered that he was, unfortunately, nearly blind with a cataract.

The sun compass is an easy instrument to use. It works in the same way as a sun dial in the garden. Instead of setting the

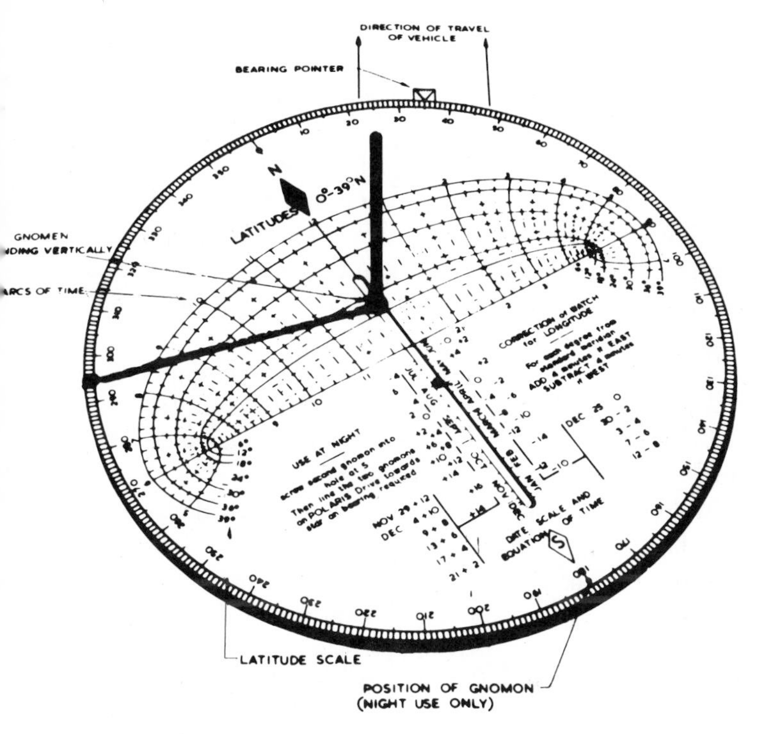

instrument at a certain bearing to find the time, the time is known from the watch, set on the compass, and the angle of travel can then be set on the instrument or determined from it. Most sun compasses give sufficient instructions on their dials, but my introduction to the instrument was most bewildering, for, while I had learnt how to use it before going on a short trip in Tripolitania, my navigation appeared hopelessly wrong. We failed in our objective to find the vital pass up the northern escarpment of the Hamada el Homra, and the feature itself seemed to be wrongly positioned on the map. My next desert journey involved a compass traverse across flat desert to the small group of palm trees of Bir el Harasc, with no features for well over 300 km. Our navigation worked perfectly, giving me immense confidence in desert navigation, and a certainty that there was something strange about the mapping of the northern escarpment of the Hamada el Homra. It was, as I discovered during a camel journey I made some years later, up to 15 km out of true geographical position.

At the end of a day's journey using a sun compass a small error might have developed, and the traveller needs to find his true position accurately so that he does not continue with that error on the following day. There is an easy way of finding the true geographical position from the stars by using a set of tables, a theodolite or bubble sextant, and by knowing the exact time. I was horrified when I first saw the computations required to fix a position, but soon realized that it was simply a matter of looking up a few tables, and doing simple addition and subtraction, no greater mathematical skill being needed. However, it is essential to learn at the home base, and work through things slowly in comfort, practising as much as possible. It is thoroughly worth the trouble, for it allows complete confidence when travelling anywhere in any bush or desert. An article by the author on both travelling by sun compass and fixing a position from the stars is to be found in the *Geographical Journal*, June 1967, pages 192–205: 'A simple method of navigating in deserts'.

However self sufficient an expedition might be, there will always be a risk that part of the team might break down and have to await rescue by another part of the expedition. This was once tried as part of a military exercise in desert training in some desolate limestone landscape between Benghazi and Jalo in Libya. Driving up from the south after spending three weeks in the south-east corner of Libya, two Land-Rovers split away from the main party, and for almost a day made slow progress over very rough country before reaching the area of the exercise. On arrival, one of the first actions was to divide and ration the food and water, while the position was calculated, and a latitude and longitude of nearly the correct co-ordinates were sent over the radio to the Royal Air Force Rescue Team. The team calculated on being 'lost' for up to three days, but knew that the air and ground search parties would soon be operating. During the day one sentry was posted at the top of a nearby hill, and he was equipped with whistle, mirror (for reflecting the sun), binoculars, compass, white flag and signal pistol; and he had the makings of a fire ready with oil to light when help was spotted. Night came without contact, and until midnight the sentry was kept on the hill, but now equipped with a powerful torch. Light and sound can travel far by night, so a fire was kept burning, and an occasional Very light sent skywards, but there was no answer. The desert seemed to be of a separate world. The following morning a Land-Rover was seen about 3 km away. It was discovered to be working along a survey line for oil, and when the two members of the little group approached on foot, the oilmen took them so much for granted that they might have been in the middle of a big city. However, water was offered, but refused by the now thirsty party, as they felt it was against the rules of the game. They regretted it next day. They had not realized when an RAF aircraft flew low over them a few times on the second day, that this was the searcher's signal for the successful completion of the exercise. The group thought otherwise, and assumed that the land party would be following shortly. Finally, instructions came over the radio that they were to return to Benghazi, but by that time water was really short, and reserves were all that was left for the journey back over 150 miles.

A search procedure was included in written safety instructions for a later expedition. They included a few notes on finding an objective in featureless terrain: 'When you have completed the leg of your journey, i.e. your milometer reads the required distance, but the objective has not appeared, stop and work out your estimated position. Then prepare to make a square search, taking care to work out bearings and distances.'

'Any fool can be uncomfortable' is sometimes quoted in the expeditionary world, and it is often the small and simple things that help towards comfort. Much about desert travel was handed down from early explorers and also from the Long Range Desert

A SQUARE SEARCH

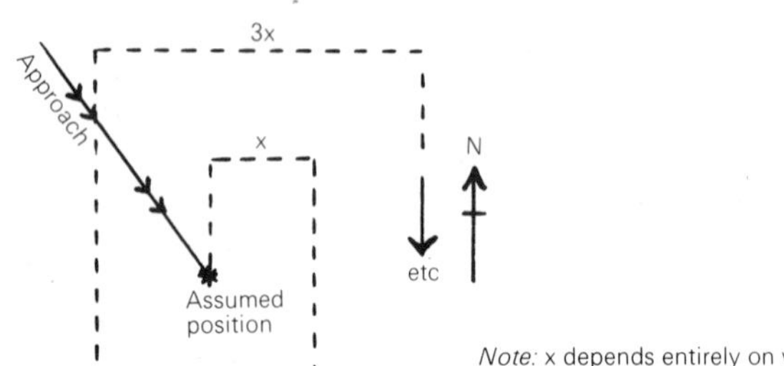

Note: x depends entirely on visibility: but could, for example, be two km.

Group during the Second World War. They discovered that one of the best ways of keeping the cold desert night winds out was to dig a grave about 300 mm deep in the sand and unroll the bedding into it. The digging warmed the body, and the grave gave protection from the wind. One doctor friend assured me that many expedition members would move their sleeping positions during the night, getting up to drag their bedding to a more centralized position near the nucleus of vehicles as though in search of the company of the remainder. It is interesting to see who establishes his base near the centre of the camp, and who goes away to seek privacy and quiet.

Most deserts have some unattractive insects, reptiles and mammals; and perhaps most commonly associated with deserts is the scorpion. However, too much danger is often attached to these little fellows whose sting causes pain and sickness for a few days, but is rarely fatal. They are said to be attracted to warmth and therefore bedding. One night on flat and featureless desert I threw my bedding down and got on with taking star sights to fix our position. Everyone was warm in bed when I finally turned in, and to my horror I found a huge and aggressive looking scorpion waiting for me when I lifted the bedding to put it into the 'grave' I had just dug. I had no idea that anything lived on this barren waste, and even suspected one of the others of having imported a practical joke. That suspicion was allayed a few hours later when I saw another one looking at me from within an empty tin only an arm's length away from my face where I was lying. I shook my shoes before putting them on next morning. I was once stung on the hand by a very small scorpion, but it was not much worse than a wasp's sting. More for the psychological effect than anything else I have always taken a mosquito net, the only disadvantage being that it reduces the clarity of the clear desert night as you look up from the warmth of a sleeping bag into the star filled space which can be seen better than from anywhere else in the world.

Food is the constant topic of conversation on most types of expeditions, often assuming unusual importance. Certain parts of a diet can become a source of acrimony unless shared fairly. I have always found that sweet things are particularly popular in hot dry climates, and on one particular expedition we had a small quantity of children's sweets which were issued to each party before going off to work each day. After someone had wrongly helped themselves to some one day, I heard one member saying that if he found the culprit he would 'lay him cold'.

Desert expeditions usually take place in winter so that less water need be carried, and less effort spent in keeping cool. However, the colder weather leads to larger appetites, and nearly all food has to be carried into the desert. An occasional gazelle can provide welcome fresh meat, although in many countries it is illegal to kill them. In others, carrying a weapon can lead to major political difficulties. Even if a desert can produce fresh meat and water it cannot produce starches; and it might well be necessary to carry sacks of flour, rice, porridge and pastas such as macaroni to provide the basis for the rations. Flour can be made into pancakes; and, if the group is sufficiently static, an oven can be improvised very easily for baking bread and pastry. Some oasis gardens produce salads, vegetables, fruit and potatoes. It is useful to have some rations packed together as complete packs so that a vehicle crew of three can find all it wants in one box for two or three days. The extra packaging required for these adds bulk and weight, but on the other hand, if made of cardboard or wood, this can be used as fuel for heating the food. One useful way of using cardboard, paper, and even camel dung is to burn it in a 'Volcano Kettle' for heating water. The fuel is fed through the top into the central chimney, and the water heated in the outer skin. If the hole at the bottom is kept facing into the wind, and if the fire is stoked constantly with cardboard, the burner becomes a small furnace and water heats rapidly. The burner does, however, get thoroughly coated with soot which seems to come off onto everything else.

Working during summer heat requires careful planning of food and water. Consumption of liquids can be as high as two gallons per man per day, and, correspondingly, the appetite falls off. In such conditions salts are washed through sweat out of the body, and if less food is being eaten, then the intake of salt is naturally less. Therefore, food should be made as appetizing as possible, extra salt should be used in cooking, and expedition members should be encouraged to take extra salt to balance their high consumption of liquids.

Many expeditions now fly into the countries where they are going to work, arriving suddenly from temperate climates into intense dry heat. Furthermore, time is often short, and they find themselves working hard in the field within a few days of arrival. The first three or four days are dangerous because the body does not indicate how much water is really needed, and the tendency is to drink too little, which can lead to dehydration and heat illnesses which can rapidly become fatal. First indications are lassitude, possibly headaches, and nausea. A salt deficiency is shown by cramps, and can quickly be remedied by taking salt and water. Clearly, heat illnesses can generally be avoided during acclimatization by planning the expedition so that a lot of water is available during the first three or four days; and members should be encouraged to drink as much as possible, and to throw it over the body to keep as cool as possible. The individual's approach is, of course, also important, and if members of the expedition are confident that they know the sensible precautions to prevent heat illnesses, if their morale is high, then there should be no problems.

The Sandhurst Archenu Expedition was in the Libyan Desert in the height of summer, and, after travelling south for two days one of the members developed diarrhoea, meaning that vital liquids were passing straight through him. Little moisture was reaching his skin's surface in sweat: and so it was getting hotter, and the body's natural cooling system had broken down. To overcome the problem he was kept in the shade, and damp clothes put over some of his skin. To make matters worse part of his skin was sunburnt, and this prevented sweating on that part of the skin. Water was cooled in canvas water bags, and he was given quantities of weak, cool orange squash with a very small quantity of salt. Subsequently the doctor confessed that he had nearly recommended calling for some form of air support to evacuate the patient, for the situation had been extremely serious.

All expeditions to any part of the world run the risk of being a liability to the local government, and to people likely to be called out to help rescue. It is the duty of all expedition leaders, therefore, to have carefully laid plans for emergencies as far as possible. Expeditions must be as well organized as possible to avoid such risks, and I have tried in this chapter to give hints to this end in desert conditions. By achieving a reasonable degree of safety and comfort an expedition is naturally more confident and better able to produce good scientific results.

5. THE POLAR REGIONS

by Wally Herbert

The choice of definition

The earth's axis is inclined to the plane of the earth's orbit around the sun at an angle of 66° 33′—consequently, on midwinter's day in the Northern Hemisphere when the tilt of the earth's axis is away from the sun, there is, theoretically, no place at sea level on or north of the Arctic Circle where the sun at midday is visible, nor is there a place on or south of the Antarctic Circle where at midnight on the same date the sun is below the horizon.

What you have here, however, is a definition of the polar boundaries from an astronomer's point of view—a definition which does not even make allowances for the refraction of light, let alone all the other factors which combine to produce a polar setting. So what we need is a more 'practical' definition, and in the case of the Antarctic the solution is simple: ignore the word as an adjective; call everything 'Antarctica' that is part of the continental land mass; and use the term 'Antarctic' for everything that lies south of the oceanic boundary known as the Antarctic Convergence, where the cold surface water surrounding the Southern Continent meets and sinks beneath the warmer waters of the Southern Ocean.

A more definite oceanic feature it would in fact be hard to find, for not only is there a sudden change in the surface temperature of the sea and a change in its colour, but there is a marked biological difference in the sea life south of the convergence and, more often than not, a bank of fog which is piled along the mixing zone like a huge grey wall. Cut through this into a clear sky beyond and you *know* you are in a different world.

The Arctic region, on the other hand, is not so easily defined. One may of course use the same oceanic criteria that are used in the south, as indeed the marine biologists do; but unlike the Antarctic Convergence which is circumpolar, the cold water boundary in the Arctic is broken up by the presence of land. Turn to the biologists and the ice physicists for a working definition and you will find that most of them regard the occurrence of permafrost as the significant and definite boundary of the Arctic, for permafrost, as its name implies, is the phenomenon of ground which is perennially frozen and this is of interest to botanists because the depth at which it appears determines to a great extent the type of vegetation the area can support. Neither of these definitions, however, is of the slightest use to the atmospheric physicists who define the Arctic as that region in which severe magnetic disturbances occur, or to the climatologists and social scientists who tend to prefer definitions that are based on temperature.

The trouble is, even the climatologists cannot agree on which isotherm marks the boundary between the temperate and the frigid zones. The mean temperature of 10°C (50°F) for the warmest month has found some favour among those who believe the treeline is the natural limit, for in many parts of the Arctic the two lines coincide; but even nature's limit needs some qualification, for there is a northern limit of coniferous forests, a northern limit of erect trees and shrubs, and a northern limit of species, so with a concept as complex as this it is not surprising that the term 'sub-Arctic' has come into use, or that the definitions of sub-Arctic are as varied and uncompromising as the parent term.

The rule of thumb

How then is it going to be possible to learn anything about the polar regions in a few thousand printed words when the subject itself refuses even to submit to a simple definition? The only way, it seems to me, is to plunge right in and generalize, and the first impression, totally false though it happens to be, is that the Arctic Basin was formed about 600 million years ago by the pressure of a cosmic thumb. This thumb made a dent 2,400 kilometres in diameter which emerged as a swelling of almost exactly the same proportion at the opposite end of the world. The Arctic Basin had then filled with water to become an almost land-locked ocean, and the bulge in the south, a continent surrounded by sea. In area the two are almost the same, each covering over thirteen million square kilometres, and the average depth of the Arctic Ocean at approximately 2,000 metres is not far short of the mean elevation of the Antarctic Continent which works out at about 2,300 metres. Nor can one ignore the fact that the greatest depth of the Arctic Ocean at 5,440 metres is only about 300 metres deeper than the height of Antarctica's highest peak. But far more surprising than the likeness in size is the 'mirror image' in shape. Superimpose on a map of one an outline of the other and, providing the two are at the same scale and the Antarctic Peninsula is laid over Greenland, incredibly they seem to fit.

Of course the value of this illustration is dubious to say the least, for not only are the similarities in size and shape purely coincidental, but the idea of a cosmic thumb is nothing short of absurd. Nevertheless, it serves to show the essential difference between the two—that one is a sea surrounded by land, the other a continent of the same size and shape at the other end of the world. Both are remnants of an ice age which the planet passed through about a million years ago, and both are swirling reservoirs of cold air and frozen water, for during the winter these polar deserts receive no heat from the sun, and in summer, although they receive as much daylight as they missed during the long polar night, cloud reflects the incoming radiation back into space and on cloudless days it is reflected by the brilliant surface of the ice.

So besides their similarities in size and shape and their relationship in latitude, they have something else in common—both have a net heat loss, and long may it remain so, for it has been estimated that should the icecaps melt (and it would require a rise in the mean annual temperature of only a few degrees) the level of the oceans would rise at least 60 metres and this would be enough to submerge almost every major city in the world and half of this planet's habitable land. This heat loss, however, must be balanced by a gain of heat in the form of warm air from the middle latitudes or the polar regions would be getting colder all the time which in the long run would be equally disastrous—consequently we have a flow of air created by the unequal heating of the earth's surface in which the polar *heat sinks*, as they are called, act not only as thermostats in maintaining the earth's heat balance, but also as one of the driving forces in the circulation of the atmosphere.

The elements

Now let us look at it from the traveller's point of view. In the Southern Ocean this circulation of air is fairly constant—flowing in a clockwise direction around the continent it combines with the currents to create those gigantic seas which the mariners call the 'roaring forties', the 'furious fifties' and the 'screaming sixties'. Not without good reason are the regions so described; but just as this barrier range of mountainous seas between latitude 40°S and the Antarctic Circle effectively barred the way to all but the most courageous of men during the latter part of the nineteenth century and the early years of the twentieth, so too do these circumpolar winds prevent the warmer air of the temperate latitudes from getting at the ice and turning the Southern Continent into a morass.

The story in the Arctic, however, is different, for in the Northern Hemisphere there is no equivalent belt of winds to keep the cold air imprisoned or to keep the warm air out, so of these two polar deserts the Antarctic is the coldest and the further inland the explorer goes the colder the climate becomes.

8. Dogs resting while on the British Trans-Arctic Expedition of 1968–9.

The lowest recorded temperature in the world was measured at the Soviet Antarctic station Vostok in 1960 when the screen temperature read −88.26°C (−126.9°F). Vostok stands some 3,050 metres above sea level near the centre of the great dome of the Antarctic plateau. Round the coast the temperatures, relatively speaking of course, are very much milder. This is partly because of the latitude and partly because of the lower altitude and the 'warming' effect of the sea.

The air above the Arctic Ocean by comparison is not nearly as cold and dry as it is over the centre of the Antarctic icecap, and the reason for this is that the thin skin of ice on the surface of the

Arctic Ocean is frequently being fractured as it drifts with the winds and currents and exposes water which in all but two months of the year is warmer at −1°C (−30.2°F) than the mean temperature of the air. During the sixteen months that the British Trans-Arctic Expedition spent on the Arctic Ocean (February 1968 to June 1969) we found that the annual accumulation of snow, measured by its water equivalent, was four and a half inches of which one and a half inches fell as rain in the months of July and August, whereas in the Antarctic the annual accumulation amounts to only two inches of water and all of that falls as fine granular crystals of 'ice'.

Relative humidity out in the centre of the Arctic Ocean in the summer is generally above 90 per cent, but, surprisingly, the presence of open water and the consequent hoar frost adds very little depth to the snow cover, much of which in any case is lifted by the winds and dumped in the open water between the ice floes or in the areas where the ice has been pressured into chaotic fields of rubble. Not that there is much wind in the central Arctic Basin—in our experience there was no significant seasonal variation in wind speed, and even during storms (which are likely to occur at any time in the year) the winds were seldom strong enough to lift the snow to eye level. The highest wind speed we recorded during the entire sixteen-months journey was only 64 kph even though drifting snow occurred on average one day in five.

The Antarctic, on the other hand, along with the record for the lowest air temperature, holds the record for the highest wind speeds. The air circulation in the Southern Ocean, as I have already said, is dominated by the fiercest westerlies found anywhere on earth, while around the perimeter of the continent the winds are predominantly east or south-easterly and influenced by the local topography. Some of these local winds are the result of cold, dense air pouring down the slopes from the polar plateau, and these winds (known as *katabatic* winds) are tremendously strong and can gust to speeds exceeding 240 kph.

At Commonwealth Bay on George V Coast, gusts of 290 kph are not uncommon, and at most coastal stations winds of 160 kph have been recorded at one time or another. As for blizzards, they have a ferocity rarely matched anywhere else on earth and to be caught out in one during the winter is an experience that no man who has survived it will ever forget. An immense amount of snow is shifted by these blizzards for, unlike the Arctic, there is nowhere, except in crevasses, where the snow can be dumped on the central plateau. Put any object in the path of such a blizzard and a drift will form in minutes and continue to build until the object is buried and the surface configuration is once again smooth—in fact, snowdrifts have been a problem on most Antarctic expeditions and many methods of deflecting the winds have been tried. The most successful are those which permit the wind free passage either by raising the huts on stilts if built on the foundations of coastal rock, or by constructing an entire station beneath the natural level of the surrounding snow plain if the station is inland.

But there are local areas in the Arctic too (outside of the Arctic Basin) where the traveller is likely at certain times of the year to be hit by a freak wind or forced to shelter from a blizzard in which the gusts reach or even exceed 160 kph. I have myself many times in North West Greenland experienced such storms. On 8 March 1972, a few hours after setting out from Thule Airbase with my wife, a friend and a team of dogs, we were caught by a wind which only a few miles away up in the hills near the airbase reached a recorded peak of 335 kph—the second highest wind speed ever recorded on the face of the earth. With what force that wind hit us it is of course impossible to say. It was certainly as violent as anything I experienced in the four years I spent in Antarctica, and there is not the slightest doubt in my mind as to which is the more hostile or hazardous environment from a traveller's point of view. This, however, I shall discuss at length later, for there are a few phenomena which it would be remiss to ignore.

First there is the clarity of the atmosphere. This can be most perplexing to the inexperienced traveller, for unlike the temperate regions, there is no industrial haze to restrict the view, and with no trees and seldom any buildings against which to measure distance, mountains, capes, even marker flags invariably turn out to be at least five times further away than they appear to be. Mirages are also common and light reflected or refracted from minute ice crystals suspended in the air create mock suns, arcs and haloes which split the shadow of a man. Then there is the *whiteout*—a phenomenon created by an overcast sky which so diffuses the light on the snow that all shadow and texture in the surface is lost and the traveller or flyer has the sensation that he is suspended in the centre of a table tennis ball. In such conditions it is not only impossible to judge distance, but even to sense the plane of the horizontal, and it is not uncommon for a standing man to become so disoriented that he actually loses his balance. I have seen a team of dogs fall over like a pack of cards, and on one occasion when sledging across a flat stretch of sea ice I had the illusion that they were climbing like flies straight up an unseen wall.

As with sight, so too with sound strange things can happen in the clear polar air. I have heard dogs howling in the Antarctic at a distance of eight miles and heard the conversation of men at a 'measured' distance of three. Then there are those frequent and often spectacular displays—the *aurora borealis* in the north and the *aurora australis* in the south: for thousands of years they have fascinated and occasionally even frightened men with their shimmering mutations of light and those faintly whispered sounds which scientists who have never been north say the observer has simply imagined. Nor can one ignore those flashes of light in the black polar night which a man can sense but never see, and the many weird hallucinations which torment a traveller in a state of physical and mental fatigue. But what scars the memory more than any of these is the cruel and penetrating COLD, for although cold has no substance, yet in the mind of man and in the marrow of his bones it scratches at his fear like a diamond scratching glass. Some men can take it—others can't, and there is no way of knowing without exposing yourself to the test.

The white invasion

The history of Arctic exploration is as much a progression towards man's mastery of his innate fear of the cold and the dark as it is of discovery in the geographical sense, and it is striking to note that in the northward thrust of the white race it was the Irish, Norwegian and Icelanders who were the pioneers—men who were unaware of the theoretical northern limit of human and animal life which had been laid down by the Greeks. They were followed in due course by men in search of fame and fortune—men who in their hearts believed that the Greeks might be right, but who were brave or foolish enough to stand their ships north in spite of this; but even the most courageous of them had at first dared only brief summer excursions into the ice-strewn seas. Of course, in time, as the boundary of the known world was pushed further back, the sailors became more familiar with the Arctic environment and took much greater risks, such as braving the terrors of the long polar night by hibernating in their ships and then, with the returning warmth of summer, venturing out on short sorties from their base. Some of these even made a study of the Eskimos' travelling techniques, although, judging by their inept attempts at sledging, their interest in the Eskimos was purely academic.

This was a period in Arctic history dominated by the British and their infatuation with the search for a short cut to the fabled riches of the East, and time and again they returned to the problem, knowing full well that the solution would be of no practical use and that the price of every small success was out of all proportion to the suffering and the sacrifice of human life. It was almost as though they had convinced themselves that there was some profound religious significance in the search for the North West Passage—that the Creator had reserved His greatest rewards for those who ventured to the uttermost ends of the earth. The same ethereal thoughts are to be found in the British attempts at the South Pole, although like the North West Passage, you have to wade through a good deal of pride and patriotic rhetoric to get at the hidden motive.

Equally well disguised was the fact that the exploration and extension of British Arctic territory provided the Royal Navy with a foe in times of peace—a challenge which contrived not only to keep the cream of the navy occupied in a noble cause, but kept Britain supplied with heroes at a time when her rampant imperialism and her ambition to influence the world was in constant need of living proof that she had what it takes to be great.

Not until the Franklin tragedy of 1845–8 and the shocking disclosure that some of these heroes had been reduced to cannibalism in their last desperate bid to stay alive, did the spotlight of public adoration shift from these naval prima donnas in the centre of the stage, to the lesser characters in the wings who in the course of scratching around for the remains of the ill-fated Franklin expedition had been quietly filling in the blanks on the map. These new heroes, however, were an entirely different breed of men—loners and adventurers most of them—men with little or no regard for the gold braid of tradition, who in the course of living and travelling with the Eskimos were fast acquiring a mastery of the polar environment, and with the North West Passage finally discovered, had set their sights on the Pole.

The 'Heroic Age', as this Pole-seeking stage was called, was a strange mixture of incompetence and courage, of honour and dignity in death and glory in defeat. It spanned the period from 1875 to 1909 when the techniques of dog sledging by a handful of explorers reached the highest level, and men, no longer fearing darkness of winter or intense cold of early spring, set out on their journeys as soon as there was twilight enough to light their way.

But no sooner had a few Europeans finally mastered the Eskimos' technique of travelling than aircraft had come on the scene, and with a quicker though no less hazardous method of reaching the more inaccessible regions, the map was soon completed. Even the reign of the pioneer aviator in those fast-changing times was short lived, for as every historian is quick to point out, war accelerates technological progress, and *two* in the space of thirty years changed not only the global balance of power, but brought for the first time into sharp focus the strategic importance of that five and a half million square miles of sea which separates the two super powers.

Poles apart

North of latitude 50° live 315 million people. Within the same radius of the South Pole live a mere 4,600 souls and half of them are temporary residents—scientists, mechanics and technicians whose familiarity with the environment is about as limited as the duration of their sojourn in the South. So because of his proximity, man has a greater stake in the Arctic. It has water and oil in abundance and the potential to affect the whole climatic balance of the Northern Hemisphere, for it is now, some scientists believe, within the capabilities of man to remove that thin skin of ice and expose the hidden sea. Of course, there are still too many gaps in our knowledge of the polar deserts and the complex interaction of oceans, air and ice to risk interfering with a lever as sensitive as the polar pack; but man is under pressure to make better use of the limited space he has on the surface of this planet, and is obliged to consider seriously the most efficient use of all these natural resources—climate included.

Here again, in a sense, the Antarctic is the opposite of the Arctic. Facing each other across that frozen no-man's-land at the top of the world are the dish antennae of the most sophisticated electronic detectors that the two most technically advanced nations can muster. Classified charts of the Arctic Ocean are webbed with the flight paths of possible missile attacks and peppered with strategic targets, and while beneath the drifting pack ice cruise nuclear-powered submarines with their lethal cargoes of atomic-warheads, high above drone the nuclear bombers on a round-the-clock alert. The ten nations operating in the Antarctic, on the other hand, are all bound by a seemingly genuine desire to live and work in peace. They are all signatories to a Treaty which sets aside the continent for the peaceful pursuit of scientific knowledge and to share this hard won knowledge for the benefit of mankind. True, the Treaty works because no nation has yet found any valuable minerals which could easily be mined and its strategic importance, by virtue of its extreme isolation and its implacable climate, is practically nil; but at least in the meantime it serves as an example of the advantages of *détente*.

An even more striking comparison, however, is in the length of time that man has lived in these remote parts of the world. In the Arctic this must be at least 30,000 years, whereas in the Antarctic man has only spent a total of fifty winters. The Southern Continent was not even discovered until 1820, and yet as long as 2,200 years ago Aristotle was arguing that just as there was a frigid zone in the vicinity of the North Pole, so there must also be a frigid zone at the opposite end of the world, for it was implicit in his concept of the earth as a perfect sphere that there was balance and symmetry throughout the world. It was equally evident to the Greeks that the temperate region in which they lived was matched by another habitable region in the Southern Hemisphere, although, as far as they were concerned, there was no possible chance of finding out for they were convinced that the two were separated by a Torrid Zone where the rocks were red hot and the sea was on the boil.

The elusive continent

Word of an Egyptian voyage down the east coast of Africa to the 'Land of Punt'—a voyage which some historians believe may have been made as early as 3000 B.C.—and of their safe return with fabulous cargoes of 'myrrh, silver, gold and dwarfs', had evidently not reached the Greeks. Nor had they heard (or had simply ignored) the story of the Phoenician circumnavigation of Africa between 600 and 597 B.C.—a voyage which antedates Bartholomew Diaz's voyage south as far as the Cape of Good Hope by over a thousand years.

The fifteenth- and sixteenth-century cartographers might at least have been expected to have moved with the times, but even they, in spite of proof that the Greeks had been wrong about the 'burning' Equator, were still too impressed by the logic of the Greeks to write off the Southern Continent. When Magellan in 1520 passed through the strait which now bears his name at the southern tip of the American continent and reported land to the south, even though he believed this land (which he called Tierra del Fuego) to be an archipelago, it was immediately taken by the geographers and cartographers of his day to be the most northerly projection of the great Southern Continent, and with each new discovery of land in the Southern Hemisphere, *Terra Australis* grew until on the charts its northern perimeter had crept north, in some places as far as the Tropic of Capricorn.

Eventually, of course, it had to shrink. In fact, during the seventeenth century there was hardly a map published that was not in some detail proved incorrect before the ink had had time to dry. Drake, when he was blown south of Cape Horn saw no land to his south; the Dutch discovered that Australia was an island and Cook sailed right around New Zealand. But still, in spite of Cook's guarded reflections on the probability of there being a Southern Continent, rumours were soon spreading that he had actually discovered it and that he had found it inhabited by people who were 'hospitable, ingenious and civil'. As a result of his second voyage in 1773–4, and his third crossing of the Antarctic Circle, however, he felt 'now well-satisfied no continent was to be found in this ocean but must lie so far south as to be wholly inaccessible on account of ice.'

This was evidently misread by the cartographers to mean that there was *no* land, and so great was the reputation of Cook that they had no alternative but to regard the Southern Continent as a myth and remove it reluctantly from their maps. In fact Cook had not been in any doubt that land existed to the south: 'I firmly believe,' he wrote, 'that there is a tract of land near the pole which is the source of most of the ice that is spread over this vast Southern Ocean.' One can therefore only assume that the geographers and map publishers of the day, disappointed at having their fertile dreamland turned to ice, wrote it off in a fit of pique. But write it off they did, and for the first time in over 2,000 years the bottom of the globe lay bare.

Forty-six years went by before any ship again crossed the Antarctic Circle for the sole purpose of discovery, and Cook's successor, Fabian von Bellingshausen, was a Russian. On 28 January 1820, while his ships were labouring through a heavy swell in latitude 69°21′S, longitude 2°14′W, he saw 'a solid stretch of ice running from east through south to west . . . an ice field strewn with hummocks,' but visibility was not good and with the weather worsening he was forced to stand his ships to the north in search of open sea. On no less than three other occasions over the next three weeks he sighted the ice-covered coastline of Antarctica without being aware of the true nature of what he saw. He was more positive about his discoveries of Peter I Island and the mountainous Alexander Island off the coast of the Antarctic Peninsula, and his charting of South Georgia, the South Shetlands and the Sandwich Islands was so accurate that his survey has only recently been improved. But oddly enough, on his return to Russia his remarkable voyage met with little acclaim. His reports and charts were not published until ten years later and were not made available outside Russia until long after the sealers had gutted the wildlife of the Scotia Sea and moved on to other grounds.

Nor was there any great rush among the other nations with sealing and whaling interests in the South to explore this new land. Eventually, however, in the late 1830s the French, American and British governments each sent out an expedition, and of the three, the British expedition was unquestionably the most successful—indeed, the leader of this expedition, James Clark Ross, was one of the most outstanding seafaring explorers the world has seen. At the time of setting out for the Antarctic he had already spent a total of seventeen summers in the Arctic; he had been a midshipman on the first expedition to survive an Arctic winter without loss of life, and during the period 1829–34 he had spent four consecutive winters in the Arctic and discovered the North Magnetic Pole. But although his Antarctic voyages resulted in the greatest geographic discoveries of the age, the British were still obsessed with the North West Passage, and not until the turn of the century did interest focus once more on the Southern Continent.

Within a decade, however, the 'heroes' had all come and gone and, as with the North, two world wars and the dramatic surge in technology changed not only the technique but the whole attitude of man towards polar exploration. Even the British who clung as nostalgically to the 'Scott tradition' as they did to the conviction that Britannia ruled the waves were, by 1957, putting their faith in machines.

There was a time in my own polar career when I cursed the aircraft which shattered the tranquillity and sense of isolation I felt on the Antarctic plateau 450 kilometres from the Pole in order to resupply my party with food and fuel. I was then undeniably a romantic. The appeal of the Antarctic for me was the adventure and the illusion that in some small way I was in the process of making history. I had returned to the Antarctic after an absence of two and a half years in the North to indulge further the passion for exploration which I had enjoyed on my first expedition; but gone were the ascetics and the 'characters' of old—men attracted by the privations and the rigours of the traditional expedition. Man the scientist had come with his retinue of servicemen and their thundering machinery. Within a few years there would not be one major glacier or mountain range that had escaped the sharp eye of the airborne camera and the scrutiny of the photo-interpreters in their cosy offices. Men would still be needed in the field to provide ground control for the aerial photos; but that last summer I spent in the Antarctic in 1962 was for me a race against time—a race to make one last exploratory journey and publish the maps before the aerial camera could beat me to the task.

The tax payers' expedition

There are some thirty-four stations at present being manned in the Antarctic by ten of the Treaty nations. Each national operation has its characteristic way of approaching the problems—some believing that cost-effectiveness is the all important criterion; others more ambitiously sparing no expense in order to get results. The National Science Foundation's budget is currently running at $25 million. The Russian programme is presumably as costly, and even the British, who traditionally have sacrificed luxuries for the privilege of going South, are finding it hard to operate their six bases these days on a budget of less than £2 million. Salaries and equipment account for only a fraction of the total. Most of it goes on logistics, and a cheap way of running an Antarctic expedition simply does not exist.

So why is so much money being poured into these operations? Prestige unquestionably is the only honest answer, for Antarctic research, like the US space programme, is sustained by politics. The NSF is now seeking to emphasize the practical potential of the Antarctic in order to fend off criticism of the cost of its Antarctic programme. Other organizations are trying to cut their costs by imposing a more rigorous and rational order of scientific priorities and by trying to improve their efficiency both at home and in the field. Others are simply making a scene over every penny that is spent in the hope that the pounds will take care of themselves, and in the process are losing the most important of all their assets—their credibility. Meanwhile, 'science for its own sake' grinds on in the South, and scientists in their embarrassment and in the hope of keeping their jobs are desperately hoping that their research may result in something which the common man can recognize as 'useful'.

Each summer sees over three thousand men and a handful of women disgorged from ships and aircraft around the coast of the continent. Roughly a third are American, another third are Russian, and the remainder a motley collection of men from the other eight nations who already have laid claim, or would like to do so, to a wedge-shaped slice of that frozen cake at the bottom of the world. The 'time-expired' fly happily out, and while the new boys are trying hard to remember the tricks of survival which they have gleaned from the crash course, seminars and films, the old hands and the administrators shuffle them around continually from one over-heated hut to another. Within a few days the field crews are bundled into planes and flown to some isolated spot to practise their professional skills, while those left swarming around the base eagerly get on with their allotted tasks. Sadly, however, this initial enthusiasm soon wears off for there is nothing the Antarctic has to offer a man who doesn't enjoy his work—'the day after arriving, the adventure is over' is a complaint often heard at McMurdo Sound. But for the graduate with a stake in his science, and those technicians, mechanics and general dog's-bodies who are energetic and by nature self-sufficient, the Antarctic is not only an outlet for their exuberance, but a unique setting in which to take a measure of themselves.

It is much the same in the Arctic at the isolated weather stations, the Distant Early Warning stations which are part of the

North American air defence system, and the scientific stations which drift about on the Arctic Ocean. All of them need technicians, mechanics, cooks and caretakers in addition to their scientific staff, and although they may not be on the same salary scale or have anything in common with each other in their home environment, nevertheless they are bound, if by nothing other than the instinct of self-preservation, to be cooperative whilst on the ice. In addition to these 'static' stations, there is plenty of field activity in the Arctic which is financed by Government grants—the Polar Continental Shelf Project is one, the Naval Arctic Research Laboratory another, and of course there are many more, some better organized and more generously backed by tax payers' money than others, but all of them in need of casual labour as well as specialists.

The advantages of going North for the first time under the protective wing of organizations such as these are obvious: they are established operators who over the years have amassed a tremendous amount of practical polar experience. They have for the most part smooth running, efficient and effective facilities geared to moving their crews around with the minimum of effort or risk. Prospecting companies also operate the pyramid principle in support of each crew in the field—indeed, it is only operations built on this sort of scale and in this particular shape which can safely take on a novice without putting the whole expedition at risk. But make no mistake—there is no room even in projects such as these for the man who does not pull his weight.

I feel I must also make clear the difference between joining a field project for the summer, and signing on for a year at some isolated Arctic weather station or a two and a half year 'tour of duty' at one of the smaller Antarctic bases. In theory, the longer the duration of the stay, the higher the calibre of the man must be—and I do not mean academically. It is not even enough that he should be a mature and self-sufficient man; a resourceful, hard-working, good-humoured man who is totally lacking in cant or bias or any political or religious convictions which are too strong to be constrained. He must be the sort of man that can always be relied upon; the sort of man who actually thrives on physical isolation and the routine of survival at some God-forsaken snowed-up base several hundreds of miles from any other human habitation.

Needless to say, the kind of men who can live in harmony on weather stations such as these are few and hard to find, for by the very nature of their jobs they cannot travel far from base and are obliged to play host to the scores of field specialists who pass through every summer. But there are a few bases in the Antarctic where it is not possible to fly men into the field and where the supply ships arrive too late in the summer for them to catch the season. At these bases the field crews must winter over in order to get an early start, and here men after my own heart get the best of both worlds. There are, however, a good many specialist scientists who regard wintering over as a complete waste of time and would rather change their field of interest than occupy themselves during the long polar night on some work for which they would receive no academic accolades.

Times have changed, and so have the men and attitudes. The polar regions still put out their challenge, and there will always be some who accept it, but the challenge is no longer directed at man, it is aimed at the organization, of which the individual is only a minute part, and the real challenge only seeks out the man when he breaks free from the protective shell of the great machine and sets out on his own.

The private expedition

The best possible introduction to the polar regions, as I have already said, is to join one of the many 'tax payers' expeditions'. Of course, until recently this was easier said than done for the United States Antarctic Research Programme was supported by the Navy; but for some reason which has never adequately been explained, the Navy has now backed out, and a private contractor, Holmes & Narver Inc., have taken over the construction work and general support facilities at the US Antarctic bases. So the way is now open for the civilian and even for Admiral Byrd's grandson who would never, so we are led to believe, have had an opportunity of getting down to the Antarctic and seeing for himself that continent a large part of which carries his grandmother's name, had it not been for Holmes & Narver. They advertise for their work force in the classified section of every large circulation newspaper in the US and it was in answer to one of these advertisements that the grandson of Byrd got a job in the Antarctic as a common labourer. The British also advertise for their Antarctic personnel and have done for years. It was in answer to an advertisement in the *Daily Telegraph* that I went to the Antarctic for the first time as a surveyor in 1955 on a two and a half year contract at a salary of £325 a year! The scientists of course do not have to suffer this sort of indignity for the personnel officers from the various polar organizations are constantly soliciting students in their final year at university to go South in search of adventure and have a PhD thrown in.

But a little knowledge is a dangerous thing, for what you learn by being a small cog in one of these enormous wheels, though useful, is not as easy to relate to the private expedition as you might imagine. The equipment and the techniques of travel, not to mention the whole complex structure upon which the field programme is based, are in a different class. There is a tendency to take all this for granted while serving the government, and it comes as a nasty shock to realize that the aircraft support you have grown accustomed to on these government sponsored projects must, in the case of the private expedition, be paid for by you unless you can think up a proposition which appeals to the Service Chiefs as something from which the Navy or the Air Force can clearly benefit.

You will also be faced sooner or later by the realities of the commercial world where the plan of an expedition is assessed not in terms of its scientific programme, but on its literary and filming potential and as a dramatic set of despatches which might be sent out from the field, and the irony of this is that the better the expedition is planned and the more likely it is to succeed, the less likely you are to raise the money to launch it.

Insurance companies, on the other hand, are more impressed by careful planning than are newspaper men. If therefore you are the sort of man who refuses to be beaten, you now try to persuade Lloyds to provide an acceptable insurance cover for the bank, who are then more favourably disposed towards giving you a bridging loan to cover the total amount that your agent has so far been able to raise in the form of promissory notes and various literary contracts. At this stage these contracts yield an advance—a mere fraction of the total amount, but one which is big enough to pay the insurance premium—and with this paid, you are in business.

The incentive to succeed is of course still personal (perhaps even patriotic), but it is now also strongly financial, for the expedition has been launched on borrowed money and the commercial sponsors are paying off their contract money in instalments. The first of these comes with the signing of the agreement, the next on setting out, and in the case of my journey across the North Pole, the third at the Pole of Relative Inaccessibility, the fourth on establishing our winter quarters, the fifth at the summit of the super mountain and the last, which is always the biggest, on finally completing the journey. Even this final instalment, however, does not relieve the expedition leader and his Committee of Management of their financial burden, for they must now pay off the interest on the bank loan and this can only be done out of lecture fees and royalties from the sale of the book.

And so in the end, the irony which struck at the start of this long road is likely these days to reappear ten times as large, for by completing the journey without loss of life, the film, the book, the lectures and articles all lack that vital ingredient—'tragedy'—without which there is little hope of climbing out of debt. Of course, for those who are prepared to improve their story by spicing it with a string of lies, and those who court disaster out of crass stupidity or through some sick obsession to 'succeed' at any cost, the result is a healthy balance sheet, but offset against this, presumably, is a certain loss of pride.

This problem is seldom encountered by the low budget summer expeditions because with these it is customary for members to contribute at least half, and sometimes three-quarters, of the total amount required. Discounts and small grants make up the balance and the odd newspaper article pays for the printing of the report; but the more ambitious polar expedition, competing for its financial backing with all the other adventurous projects which are in search of sponsorhip, is at a disadvantage, firstly because it is usually too long in the field to sustain a public interest, and secondly because the armchair explorer as a rule prefers vicarious excitement in the form of a mountain, sea or jungle adventure rather than the vicarious fatigue, hunger, cold and misery encountered on a protracted polar trek.

But supposing, in spite of all that I have said, a polar expedition strikes you as more challenging than the many alternative ways of having a bad time—how do you begin? Take, for example, the first surface crossing of the Arctic Ocean—a journey of sixteen months and almost 6,000 kilometres: before even thinking of attempting this journey I had spent four years in the Antarctic and sledged some 9,700 kilometres with dogs over every kind of Antarctic terrain and type of floating ice, and my three chosen companions for the trans-Arctic trek, although with less mileage behind them than me, were all seasoned polar travellers with between them a total of seventeen winters' and thirty-six summers' experience. Nevertheless, it seemed to me essential that we should test our techniques and temperament in an Arctic setting, and I chose for this purpose to winter with the

9. Crossing a lead with dog in sledge boat.

Polar Eskimos in North West Greenland from where, in the spring of 1967, we made a dog sledging journey of 2,415 kilometres over some of the roughest country you can find anywhere in the North in an effort to test our equipment to destruction and find the weakness in our resolve.

That training period, together with the time I spent researching, planning and trying to raise the £50,000 that was needed to launch the expedition, occupied four years of full-time work, and by the time the expedition set off from Alaska I had studied *every* book that had been written during the past 360 years by explorers who had seen or travelled on the polar pack and every scientific paper that was of any relevance to my study of the pack ice environment. But although, on the basis of this research, I had chosen a route across the longest axis of the Arctic

Ocean which would benefit from the drift of ice and checked out my predictions and plans with every living expert in the western world, still there remained a great many uncertainties for no one had ever travelled as far or for as long as we were proposing to do.

Risks of course are all part of the game, but every one must be calculated and every nightmare analysed for those weaknesses in your plan which presumably gave rise to them. You are even permitted to fail providing that your failure is the result of some vindictive twist of fate which was impossible to foresee; but to fail because of an error of judgement, or because you were too lazy or too cocksure to research your subject thoroughly and test your equipment and techniques before setting out on a polar expedition is inexcusable.

Even so, the history of polar exploration is more a record of failure than it is of success. Franklin, De Long, Andree and Scott are a few notable examples, and there are many others, more fortunate than these, who survived with no more than a wound to their pride which was quickly healed by the balm of fame and a small fortune in royalties and lecture fees. What then is the argument against risking your life and the lives of your

10. Repairing a broken sledge.

companions in pursuit of a goal which is beyond your reach? The official answer is that the government will have to launch a costly search and rescue operation and that other lives will be put at risk. But there is another objection running parallel to this—an objection to failure on principle. If this objection is foremost in your mind, and if you are prepared to spend some time on your research and on training, testing and thoroughly re-assessing your plans before committing yourself and your companions to some hazardous polar journey, you will, providing that you can overcome the weaknesses inherent in man, finally succeed.

As for whether a private expedition should attempt to carry out a scientific programme, this will depend on the nature of the expedition, and the only advice I can give is that science and adventure *do* go together; but—as history will show—very rarely. If what you are proposing is a 'pioneer' journey, then the information that you bring back is bound to be of value and your sense of achievement as a result so much the greater for that. But to jeopardize your chances of success by wasting time on some scientific project which could far more efficiently be done by one of the government surveys is irresponsible, to say the least. Your priorities must be clear in your mind and you must state them at the outset proudly and unequivocally, for achievement, after all, is not simply a measure of success, it is a measure also of the integrity of those who brought it off.

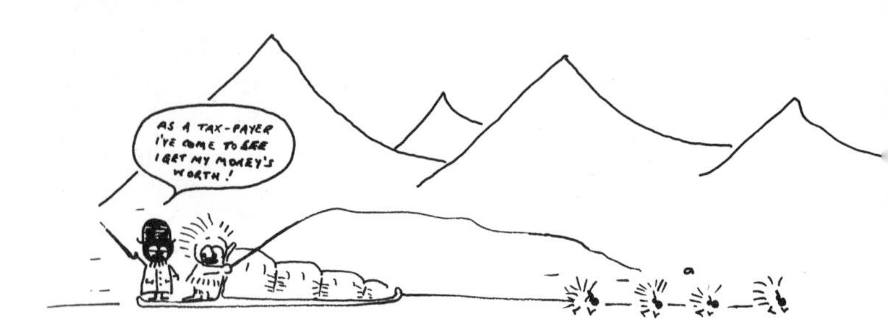

6. UNDERWATER EXPLORATION

by Christopher Roads

The canopied 6-metre inflatable with its two 35 hp Mercury outboards is proceeding cautiously through an area of shallow coral in the full knowledge that one collision, with its almost certain penetration of the fabric, will cause—to put it at its most unromantic—a severe administrative problem, since the nearest town lies over 160 kilometres away along the Sudanese coast. Bearings are taken under the blazing sun across the shimmering sea to distant peaks almost lost in heavy haze: if the mountains have been correctly identified, the resected bearings show that the heavily laden boat, with its 100 gallons of fuel and 100 gallons of water, is at last in position for its next point dive. It is the work of only a moment for a diver to sling the straps of an aqualung over his shoulders and to slip into the tepid sea. The survey continues as the diver rapidly sketches with a lead pencil on formica boards the broad configuration of the reef and notes coral species and areas of depredation. Any coral unfamiliar to the diver is immediately put in the plastic collecting pail, while a second diver carefully photographs other examples of the same coral in situ: the time allowance may be only a half hour and the next planned dive two miles away. It could be that sampling the reefs of the coast will continue into darkness, though if it does there will be very little boat movement involved.

In every way this is a typical underwater expedition but the general intention is not always one of underwater survey. In Kaafjord in the summer of 1974 inflatable craft sped up and down the fjord from a fixed base camp on the steep slope at the fjord's head. Divers heavily dressed in unisuits or two-layer wetsuits followed each other, combing the deep, cold bed of the fjord for 'anomalies' which might offer evidence of the X-craft that had attacked Tirpitz over thirty years earlier.

Both these expeditions had in common the scientific dedication of their members and reliance upon technical experts. Both required endurance, but in other ways they represent the opposite ends of the underwater spectrum:

1. Expeditions which are largely fixed in single areas involving locally intensive search, survey or experimentation.
2. Expeditions which are essentially based on movement at sea with dispersed underwater activity.

Anyone planning an underwater expedition should realize the difference in administrative demands of these differing patterns, remembering that those in (2) can be extremely taxing in logistic terms if taking place in a remote area.

The types of activity occurring in either type of expedition can be very varied, but all activity underwater at night calls for special consideration and techniques. To take a simple example: in the tropics at night it is possible to encounter severe stinging plankton in the water which are so uncomfortable for divers, whether suited or unsuited, that it simply isn't possible for them to remain in the water for more than a few minutes.

Underwater activity will usually fall into one of the following types:

1. Searching or survey—where the incidence of certain species is being assessed, inadequate charts are being supplemented or a wreck is to be located.
2. Collecting—although this might occasionally be applied to salvage, it usually denotes the collection of marine organisms for laboratory, aquarium or museum purposes.
3. Photographic—underwater photography is invaluable for base line or other environmental record purposes, but it may also be for commercial or quasi-commercial ends.

4. Physical evaluation—the object of an expedition can be to evaluate equipment or to monitor human response or endurance. Sometimes it can be the study of currents, temperature, salinity or tidal data.

While these categories constitute a starting point in the planning of a worthwhile underwater expedition, they are non-exclusive and are of most value to thinking straight when establishing clear priorities in the selection of expedition personnel. Nothing is more important in the setting up and the running of an underwater expedition than assembling the right teams. The leader must be aware of the danger of an individual, however well-qualified, pursuing his own research and causing discontent among the expedition as a whole. Although a scientist may be included because of his academic qualifications in one particular field he may be unable to apply himself in other disciplines.

Long experience of underwater expeditions has led me to prefer training existing specialists to dive rather than to hope that divers can become scientists or specialists. No large underwater expedition can escape including some very competent engineers, usually electrical as well as mechanical, as well as scientists who reflect all the disciplinary facets required. It is not possible, if the end product is to be acceptable, to expect ecologists to be good zoologists or physiologists to perform as biochemists.

The subject of expedition leadership deserves a book on its own. In this context, however, the one point that must be made is that often the most realistic solution is to have both scientific and administrative leaders, with overall authority in the hands of the latter. This does not excuse the administrative leader from doing his best to provide overall scientific policy guidance, but it does mean that he must be careful not to embarrass his scientific colleagues by imposing his own scientific judgements over subjects of which he has limited knowledge. Nevertheless in the final analysis only one man can lead, and he must both be allowed and be able to do so.

No one who has led an underwater expedition will ever be short of advice on what boats to use for the purpose. Here, as is usually the case, I am concerned with smaller boats. Most used today is the inflatable. It has many obvious advantages which have led to its very successful use on occasions, as on the Zaïre River Expedition, but equally it has some severe drawbacks under certain conditions. It is least useful in coral areas. In 1969, in a *Zodiac Mk V*, I struck a reef at about 6 knots at night. There were eighteen tears or gashes in the fabric which took a great deal of repairing but, on the credit side, only one of the five air compartments was punctured so there was no danger to life. Such an impact is rare, much more common is the puncturing of the inflatable keel from small pieces of coral getting sandwiched between the boards and the fabric. If any coral is taken on board some inevitably drops through the boards and the only course open is to dismantle the boat and then reassemble it. With a large inflatable this is a strenuous task for three people and takes half a day. Moreover, in the tropics no available adhesive holds as well as factory repairs. Another great disadvantage of inflatables is that in their articulation through rough seas the whole cargo is on the move so that immense care is needed to avoid danger to the pontoons from sharp-edged items such as stowed anchors or even fuel jerrycans. It becomes necessary to have long heavy-duty canvas covers made to fit the whole way down the inside of the pontoons. The inflatable has another, though lesser, drawback in expeditionary use. The transom is scarcely long enough to accommodate two outboard motors and the pitot head for the log as well as the transducer of the echo sounder, and no other part of the boat lends itself to any of these purposes. There is no limitation, however, on the mounting of a canopy and many of our sea journeys in the Red Sea would have been impossible without one.

The aluminium alloy boat is ideal in coral areas especially

when double-skinned and filled with foam. It will stand up to quite severe impact with coral and no special care is required in cargo stowage. In order, however, to render it reasonably seaworthy with a heavy load, a canopy is essential. From personal experience I recommend one of hooped iron and heavy-duty canvas extending about one third of the way back from the bows. Its attachment to the boat is critical, and only a double row of rivets—pop rivets will do—with strips of alloy, will suffice and the centres need to be no greater than 2–3 inches apart. The disadvantages of an aluminium alloy boat are its weight and its very limited availability—the pattern most commonly to be found is the 5 metre British Army assault craft. This will require some modifications to the transom to mount two heavy outboard motors.

Fibre glass (GRP) boats are an obvious possibility. In many specifications they have the disadvantage that in persistent tropical sun the fibre glass begins to deteriorate. They certainly possess the great virtue of lightness but, while probably more easily repaired in the field than any other type of boat, they are relatively easily holed. More durable, at least in one sense, are timber boats with a sheath of GRP. They have the edge over those of painted or oiled timber which need a great deal of maintenance if they are exposed to tropical conditions.

The deficiencies of the inflatable can be, to a great extent, discounted by use of the type which has a solid lower hull from a specification originally developed for inshore rescue work. They lose most of their portability but they can prove a very attractive proposition. The true inflatable has its most perfect form and size in the *Zodiac Mk 11* with a 20 hp outboard.

If it is impossible to make landfall at night and you need more space in the boat, you can float out on lines some of your containers of fuel and fresh water. Gas cylinders also float very well. Don't forget to tie the lines of floating containers in such a way that they do not clatter together all night. If they do sleep will be impossible.

Regardless of what kind of boat you select, it is highly desirable to carry a spare motor. Johnson outboard motors and most motors, other than Mercury, can shear a pin and lose their drive while Mercurys can, but much less frequently, strip the rubber bush. It requires a motor of surprisingly small size to move a boat at 2 or 3 knots and this is preferable to becoming a complete casualty. In terms of outboards it can be argued that the Mercury is the best bet for coral areas since light accidental collisions with the coral are quite common and its final drive usually stands up to them without difficulty. Thus with the Mercury there is less risk of being swept onto a barrier reef: there would be no time in these circumstances to put in a new shear pin. From the engineering and maintenance point of view, however, Mercurys are the least attractive as they seem to have been deliberately designed so that a fully equipped, specialist workshop is necessary. There is much to be said in favour of the British Ministry of Defence preference for 40 hp Johnsons.

In general terms the outboard motor is very suitable for expeditionary use but if you want to use it daily over long periods of time, the inboard diesel is much more satisfactory and more economical. Don't forget that diesel is quite safe, whereas petrol in a small boat in which you are living and cooking under very compressed conditions is undoubtedly a hazard.

Reading equipment manuals is vitally important; in my experience few things cause greater loss of time or incur more expense than the consequences of expedition members, even engineers, failing to read manuals because they believe they know all the answers. Coupled with this is the practical difficulty of getting maintenance schedules carried out with the exactitude that contributes to real reliability. Oiling, greasing and painting are unglamorous and can always be put off until tomorrow. Unfortunately they are essential and cannot be treated casually, and nowhere is this more true than in a marine environment. It takes very little time—perhaps only three days of inattention—and an engine will seize solid: a little longer and the main steering pivot will lock immovably. Whatever else you do or don't do, a clear coding/labelling system is vital, showing that outboard petrol definitely has had the appropriate quantity of oil added.

Generally a boat conventionally navigated and powered is all that is needed for expedition purposes. In coral-infested waters the helmsman is well advised to post a lookout forward to call back information on coral heads and reef outcrops ahead. It is essential that the helmsman and lookout agree beforehand whether the lookout is calling back details of where the obstructions lie or whether he is giving instructions on which way to steer to avoid them. Many an otherwise avoidable impact has arisen from confusion on this point. A lookout may not be essential in the middle part of the day but when moving into the sun two lookouts—one from either side—is far from excessive. It is almost impossible to see coral just below the surface for two hours before sunset when going west.

If in spite of all efforts to avoid it, when darkness falls you are left in such a position that it is essential to continue to navigate a difficult coral area, it is not sufficient with most equipment to rely on an echo-sounder to give warning of coral ahead. It may be a case of finding a narrow passage through an area of coral reefs. There is only one course of action open and it is one I have used. A team member is suspended over the bows, equipped with mask, snorkel and an underwater spotlight (preferably drawing its power through cables from a power source on board). He acts as an underwater lookout and calls back directions: the helmsman, for his part, keeps the speed down to a comfortable 2 knots. A danger that must be avoided is having the lookout swept under the boat, and he must have a safety line attached. I can testify from personal experience how unpleasant it is to lose your grip, slide remorselessly along the underside of the boat and, miraculously, between the rotating twin propellers. Not everyone could count on coming through this experience entirely unscathed.

Individual movement underwater by towing is a widely recognized technique. There are, however, many locations where boats cannot penetrate or where they are insufficiently flexible. One possible solution is to use hovercraft and this I have done fairly extensively. In coral areas the type of hovercraft most able to transit areas with fingers of coral jutting above the surface is the very light single-seater. Certainly the heavier the craft the more likely there is to be skirt damage. Limitations on the use of hovercraft in underwater expeditions stem not so much from any design inadequacy as from the acute problems of salt water corrosion. Few seem to be adequately adapted for heavy daily use, though for occasional use they have many advantages. Perhaps their biggest drawback is their relatively light payload, especially when in use in the tropics where a considerable reserve of water is desirable.

More common means of mechanizing the movement of individuals are by the use of diver-propelled vehicles (DPVs). Broadly these divide into two classes; those which are restricted to the surface and up to about 1 metre below and those which can range freely. On the face of it the second category would seem preferable. These are powered by electricity, usually from high performance aircraft type lead acid 12 volt batteries. They usually have only one control—a start/stop lever incorporated in one of the two handles on either side of the propeller, as most, though not all, are 'pusher' configuration. My first experience of one of these was memorable. Over the side of our main vessel the 35 kg brightly painted, torpedo-shaped electric tug was carefully lowered on ropes. As soon as it was about a foot below the surface I climbed over the side of the boat, already wearing mask, breathing tube and flippers, cast off the ropes, grasped the handles and pulled the lever. There was a deafening explosion. Stunned, blinded, I felt myself travelling somewhere at high speed. Two or three seconds later my mind and vision cleared. I had hit the bottom 10 metres down still holding the heavy rear section—now an open shell. The front section we later recovered about 7 metres away. Remarkably neither I nor any of my companions was injured but my views on electric tugs became somewhat biased. The explanation came later. With a differential in temperature between the charging room and the deck of perhaps 5°C+, even the non-spill batteries were not impervious to electrolite spillage as it increases substantially in volume on heating. The acid acted on the alloy interior to produce hydrogen and though we had vented the tug within a very few minutes of use, hydrogen was being generated at such a pace that it was highly explosive within about five minutes.

In reasonably clear water all that you need is a means of driving yourself along just under the surface. This does not necessarily mean an electric tug. It is immense fun to roll and perform all manner of aquabatic manoeuvres with them but this is a bonus. Their disadvantage, apart from a tendency to explode, is the weight which is so great that it is almost impossible for one person to lift it in and out of the boat, while the long charging time and comparatively short running time are anything but attractive. A tug using a two-stroke engine is in a completely different category. Its two disadvantages are its restriction to not more than 1 metre below the surface and the fact that when training, it will not usually be tolerated in swimming baths since it exhausts into the water. On the other side of the coin the ICE (Internal Combustion Engine) tug is extremely light and portable at only 7 kg, and it has a fully underwater range of about 9 kilometres. It is perfectly feasible to carry extra fuel to increase this figure to 18–24 kilometres. Both types of tug can be used to mount cine or still cameras and there is no significant vibratory or noise factor with either type. Both can carry lights, or light beacons, at night and all manner of scientific apparatus, including specimen containers. The practical limitation on the use of tugs is the physical condition of the diver, provided that he does not so incline himself that he is directly in the wash of the propeller. To do so is to invite a chronic muscular pain in the stomach region.

The individual expedition member's greatest enemy is the cold. It is possible, to a degree, to ignore cold—we used to dive in the Mediterranean at depths well over 40 metres with no suit at all, teeth chattering the while—but it is unwise to do so since efficiency falls off rapidly. On the other hand I have seen a fully-suited diver on a boat in the Australian Great Barrier Reef in a state of collapse from the heat. However much of a bore, you should dress or undress according to conditions. In Arctic or near freezing conditions this means, ideally, wearing a unisuit (with track suit underneath), which is a dry suit built rather on the lines of a wetsuit. To my mind the least pleasant aspect of wearing what amounts to a double thickness wetsuit is its heavy constriction of the chest, since you want a good fit to minimize the amount of water in the suit. The alternative, and not quite so comfortable, is a 6 mm wetsuit with the trousers cut very high so that they are virtually like overalls with shoulder straps. One problem is covering the hands—gloves tend to have to be so thin that it's only a few minutes before your hands are numb with cold; mittens can be thicker but are useless for operating complex camera or similar controls.

In temperate waters, depending on the time of the year and the length of time you are under water, recommended wear is a wetsuit with or without all accessories. If you can afford it a lined suit is much better than an unlined one and, generally speaking, it is easier to leave off items than to discover that you need them on site. There is much to be said in favour of having one or two patch pockets on the thigh so that small instruments, etc., can be carried without fear of losing them.

In the tropics it is necessary to operate in accordance with obvious factors. In the winter the water temperature may only be in the lower twenties centigrade which must mean a full or half wetsuit if the stay under water is of any duration. Where the temperature is over about 26–29°C—for example, in summer in the central Red Sea the water temperature on average is 31°C—no suit is required. Indeed, in these high temperatures—

11. The Cambridge Coral Starfish Research Group's laboratory platform above the Red Sea coral.

up to 35°C at times and with the temperature at 50 metres still around 27°C—you can remain in the water for as long as 8 hours continuously without feeling cold. On the other hand your skin goes very soft and you cut easily. Wearing nothing but swimming trunks is the least tiring of all and is in very marked contrast to fatigue caused by wearing a wetsuit. If you are going to be under water for a long time, make sure your trunks are comfortable, otherwise rashes will result; they should be of light, quick-drying material without heavy elastication.

To whatever dress dictated by climatic conditions there must be added the essential individual items. The mask should be comfortable and seal well and wherever appropriate the glass should be optically ground. No expedition member is pulling his weight if he cannot see very well under water in bad light: if he needs glasses normally he needs an optically ground mask. The breathing tube must be of a reasonable bore and comfortable in the mouth: there should only be a valve on the top if you are diving in the Dead Sea—no other excuse can be accepted other than that the water in which you are obliged to dive is so noxious that it must be kept out of your mouth. Flippers or fins should fit over the whole bottom of the foot and should be a very slack fit: it may be necessary to have two pairs if you want to be comfortable both with and without wetsuit boots. The size of the flipper blade is entirely a question of your physique: it is probably better to have a smaller rather than larger pattern if in doubt. Floating flippers may seem something of a luxury but pay off handsomely if you're caught by the Pacific surf, in an instant lose almost everything, and are trying to recover your equipment in the foaming water.

Mask, breathing tube and flippers are essentials; so too is a diving knife. It is much more likely that you will save your life by cutting yourself free from some obstruction than by killing an attacking shark. A good knife should have a very sharp stainless steel blade of reasonable length, together with a handle you can grasp easily. The scabbard should be worn on the lower leg not on the thigh.

Additional useful items of equipment include a depth gauge, compass, thermometer, lifejacket, water bottle (a sensible acquisition for everyone in the tropics), a floating radio on the international distress frequency, and a small waterproof pack of distress flares or rockets. The depth gauge should be of the oil-filled type and the *Fenzy* pattern of lifejacket is much better than any other. Our tropical expeditionary practice is to recommend the wearing of lifejackets only when aqualung diving or when snorkelling on your own. This way the individual is not impeded and tired by wearing a jacket unnecessarily and, when it is needed, the jacket is in good order.

Hazards exist—there is no merit in closing your eyes to them—and a few relatively inexpensive precautions mean the difference between living and dying. No expedition leader of any experience could fail to cite instances where serious consequences have been avoided only because it has become automatic to carry certain emergency stores that are invariably carried in every boat. These should at least include water, food, a first aid kit and distress flares. You should be informed about air and temperature ranges likely to be encountered and about the presence of strong currents, the likelihood of storms—their probable duration and type—and the extent of underwater visibility. To a limited extent, it may be possible to answer some queries from the Admiralty's Pilots but up-to-date local knowledge is preferable. Easily overlooked but equally significant is the sun. Tropical sun with no cloud cover at sea level is so much more intense than, say, that of the Mediterranean that no liberties should be taken with it. Where the fair-skinned are concerned there is no substitute for graduated exposure, using, where necessary, UV barrier creams. Care should be taken that all skin areas likely to be exposed are tanned progressively. The briefer the swimming trunks the less likely that large areas of untanned skin will be later exposed through the rucking or tearing of the material.

Once away from the boat and in the water, hazards multiply. Many massive books have been written on dangerous marine animals but no one can be expected to take them in without some assistance. After cold, the biggest serious hazard is probably the diver's own forgetfulness. It is very easy to fail to look at your pressure gauge when totally captivated by the beauty of the underwater world or when utterly absorbed in some scientific experiment. It is just as easy to forget some vital piece of equipment—such as the depth gauge—and leave to guesswork rather than scientific calculation the times of your decompression stops.

Danger can lurk in various stinging animals and, particularly, in a few which attack with their teeth. Most jelly fish only sting slightly, if at all. Important exceptions include the Portuguese man-'o-war and the Australian *cubo medusae* or sea wasps.

Broadly speaking, avoid jelly fish with pronounced 'streamers' as they are more likely to sting badly. Only one jelly fish, the Australian sea wasp, of which in fact there is more than one species, has a sting which is often fatal. There is a good deal of truth in statements that it is more of a real hazard than the shark in Australia. The purple ringed octopus, again found in Australian waters, can also cause death. The answer is simple: avoid them, likewise sea snakes and marine crocodiles. Leave their investigation to expert zoologists.

It is far more difficult to avoid echinoderms, nearly all of which can inflict painful wounds. Most spines are so brittle that they almost invariably break off in the flesh. Some are also venomous: a few are extremely painful, not to say disabling. On one occasion one of my diving companions volunteered to arrange a sea urchin of the most beautiful colouring so that I could film it more easily at night. Somehow his hand slipped and he was lanced in the finger by a single spine of *Echinothrix diadema*. He was doubled up in pain almost immediately and soon began to cyanose in the finger and hand. He thought his life might be at risk and it was no comfort to know that not only were we one and a half hours distant from any form of medical assistance but that even a modern hospital would not be able to do much for him. For over an hour he endured excruciating pain before it slowly eased and for months he remembered that night.

There are minor hazards the tropical expedition member will learn quite quickly to identify and avoid: fire corals sting just like nettles and so too do hydroids; plankton can at times be full of micro-stinging organisms but it is usually at night that these are really unpleasant. There are a few far more serious hazards to which you should pay attention but which do not merit a panic response. The Mediterranean rascasse has spines which inflict painful wounds, as does the weaver in the North Sea, but both pale before the stonefish in the tropics. This is extremely venomous and sometimes very common. Anti-venoms are now available against its poison and should certainly be carried by expeditions working in shallow sea water where wading is involved.

Anyone who has closely examined the jaws of a large barracuda won't be keen to meet one in an ill humour. Traditions vary about their conduct: the truth seems to be that while at least thirty attacks on humans have been logged, they have probably been more the product of the fish going for something bright, like polished metal, or something fishlike suspended through the surface. The answer is to avoid swimming without a mask in such areas and to avoid carrying large lure-like objects.

Sharks seem to vary in conduct according to factors so complex that I can only comment on them from my own experience: first, common sharks, such as the white and black tip reef sharks, are very rarely aggressive unless severely provoked; secondly, most other sharks are rare in areas likely to be covered by any expedition working off-coast or off-shore facilities; and thirdly, most recorded shark attacks seem to suggest the agency of a rogue shark. Extensive studies in Australia seem to suggest that the danger of attack is highest in areas of low underwater visibility, in comparatively cold water and quite often in very shallow water. Perhaps the most outstanding of all underwater fishermen with whom I have swum used to go out once a week to shoot shark. To attract them to close in on him he shot smaller fish and adopted every device including leaving wounded fish pirouetting around him. About once in twenty-five such fishing trips he got a little more than he bargained for and the shark turned its attentions seriously on him. In the course of our research activity in the Red Sea I have shot a number of shark under water—in every case the stomach proved to be empty on dissection—perhaps hunger sharpens their interest in the diver or the fish that he has shot. In terms of practical advice, the spillage of blood under water seems less likely to lead to shark attack than other apparently less obvious provocations. Certain vibration frequencies certainly attract them. On one occasion I attracted a shark so quickly by this method that I was unable to raise my camera in time to film it.

It is against the certain injuries that you should really be prepared. No one can spend many days in a coral sea without getting cuts. Few can be involved in more than two or three expeditions without getting some kind of skin or stomach upset. And few have ears which give no trouble in tropical seas. The answer is a well-equipped medical chest and a fairly rigidly imposed régime of preventative medicine. For cuts caused by coral you can either paint them with friar's balsam or with mercurichrome. For ears it is essential that they are washed in fresh water with a dropper or small syringe after every period in the water. If they begin to get sore, immediate recourse to antibiotic ear drops is essential. Ear troubles are by far the worst scourge of tropical underwater expeditions: beyond a certain point you are on pain-killing tablets all the time and in such distress that you can neither sleep nor eat as moving the jaw is so painful. On the whole I would advise wider spectrum drops—antibiotic, anti-fungal and anti-bacterial—for the communal medicine chest. The treatment of skin infections of a kind which seem to arise, but fortunately rarely, from prolonged immersion, seems to require general rather than local antibiotics. In almost every other respect there are no special medical needs for underwater expeditions, that is if one excludes the consequences of failures to decompress properly. These are so important and so well covered that I must refer the reader to the *British Sub-Aqua Club Handbook*.

No one who has been on a long expedition when supplies of fresh food are very nearly non-existent or who has tried to exist on a native diet will have failed to observe the marked run down in physical capacity and energy which ultimately sets in. It is important, in terms of achieving one's expeditionary objective, to eat a reasonably balanced diet and it is essential to include some fresh fruit and vegetables. We have found that the only really durable fruits at sea are grapefruit and oranges. Even when after three or four weeks in extreme heat these are shrunken and like bullets, provided you have a hacksaw available to cut into them they can still be eaten and enjoyed. For the main part of the diet there is very much to be said in favour of British military composite rations—'compo'—provided that the variant menus are available. Assault rations are less attractive but well worth carrying for emergency purposes. If composite rations—or rations modelled on them—are used, the best way of stretching them is to 'live off the land'. The obvious method is to fish by trolling from the boat in likely areas but trolling is no good when your speed goes over $3\frac{1}{2}$–4 knots. The best method, in the sense that it avoids the possible killing of unwanted fish, is by harpooning with an underwater gun. Most fish are edible at a pinch but there are a few to avoid. It is a reasonable rule of thumb to avoid the bright coloured fish which live in coral reefs—many of these, if not actually poisonous, taste abominable. Water is the most important element in your diet and no portable solar still that I have tried could really be depended on for a supply of fresh water direct from the sea for more than a short period. On the other hand, if you are under water all day long you need very little water. It is quite practical to plan a tropical underwater expedition on the basis of 2.5 litres of water per person per day if space is really at a premium. It is possible to live for all purposes on 0.5–0.75 litres per person per day. The use of flexible 4-gallon translucent water containers is the obvious course for an expedition in small boats, but these do have the disadvantage of transmitting light causing considerable green algal growth which may later be off-putting. You must have a reasonable safety margin to allow for the loss of some containers from accidental rupture.

Everything that has been discussed so far amounts to getting and keeping a fit team in the field in a condition to be effective. If the expeditionary objective depends on searching, then there is more to it than stopping occasionally to drop a diver overboard or even fielding a line of snorkellers swimming side by side.

Searching by spot diving or by line abreast are recognized techniques but neither is normally as useful as searching with one, two or even three divers or snorkellers towed behind the main boat. Each requires no more than a simple wooden cross piece on the end of his rope. If the object is simply to find something—a shoal of fish, a reef, a particular type of bottom or a wreck—and visibility is reasonable, this method may be very effective. If it is for surveying purposes, such as what range of fauna is to be found, what species of corals, any form of quantitative or qualitive analysis, then this method begins to fail as no observer can mentally store all the data he is collecting, especially if precise locations are relevant. Under these circumstances a communications set is fixed between observer and boat. The observer gives a running commentary which is either tape recorded, or received and immediately converted into note form in the boat. In a two-way conversation the person in the boat can ask for necessary clarification and he can, in any case, add to the notes or record running data on precise locations from the boat's navigational equipment. We have used this method extensively in the Red Sea. It works admirably, especially with the observer using an aqualung, but it is important that the observer should not inadvertently ascend without breathing out. This problem we overcame by insisting on a non-stop running commentary.

Once the general search has narrowed the area under study to reasonable limits, searching can continue either with swimmers, with divers or swimmers using tugs. If specimen collection features prominently—and it must frequently do so as it represents the only way of checking identifications—unless the party is exceptionally well qualified, then a very good supply of plastic buckets with lids, of smaller containers, plastic bags and, possibly, of string bags is needed. Put as much as possible in sealed containers since not only will it keep in better condition but it will avoid the possibility, where the diver is not wearing a suit, of his being stung or spiked. Containers of larger size have an infuriating habit of splitting—at least we have not been able to find a plastic pail which will last more than a few weeks—so it is advisable to have a large reserve of them. The physical part of collecting will usually be by hand, sometimes gloved. With corals a hammer and even a chisel are useful tools. For small fish, a clean plastic bag and a small net and for larger ones, a small harpoon gun are normal. The best type of harpoon gun for easy maintenance is probably the simple rubber gun. The rubbers and junction wire are about the only spares needed and they can be interchanged by anyone in a moment. The physical effort required to load them becomes demanding only in large guns of this type. For those prepared to maintain them the oil and water type of gun can be more convenient because in their smallest, but still usable, form they are very compact. For the collection of larger fish, including shark, the ideal gun is the cartridge powered Johnson *SMG Magnum*.

Once the specimens have been brought to your boat their preservation begins, either by the use of formalin, alcohol, some other preservative type solution or by drying. If by drying, the fish need degutting—unless they are very small—and cutting or hacking in thin slices. One should, even in the tropical sun, aim to keep the pieces not above 1.3 cm thick if one wishes to ensure that drying yields good results. Neglect of these guidelines will lead to the flesh becoming infested with maggots, unless—as virtually never happens under expeditionary conditions—you have some kind of flyproof drying area available.

No expedition should fail to consider the alternative, or complement, to specimen collection, namely, record photography. Equally no expedition leader should accept a terrestrial photographer's assurance that he can convert to underwater operation until he has demonstrated conclusively that he can. Judging distance under water is an acquired skill. So far as expeditions are concerned the points to emphasize are: know your equipment, stick to reasonably well tried formulae and don't be too ambitious. It is better by far to take fairly good pictures with the versatile Nikonos or Calypso/Nikonos than to become a prima donna with a 6 by 6 cm Rollei in its massive underwater housing. The Nikonos wins hands down in its extreme portability: it can be carried all the time and is therefore always available. It is worth noting here that in underwater photography, where with flash you are trying to get a fully realistic colour rendering, exposed film should not only be kept totally dry but it should not be allowed to get too hot. Excessive heat will tend to produce a cast. Underwater cinephotography can be quite rewarding in super 8 or even in standard 8 when the lens is of high quality but it definitely falls short of the quality attainable with a 35 mm Nikonos when record purposes are the object. With 16 mm, filming under water becomes competitive but fully versatile underwater cameras are very expensive and so is the film stock. Over a period of six seasons in expeditions in the Red Sea we have developed a very effective 16 mm underwater cine camera case with reflex viewing but, even after major involvement in designing it, I still find each year that I am not really getting the best out of it until I have shot about a thousand feet of film.

The sole purpose of an expedition may be the surveying of an area for which published data is extremely scanty. In my experience accurate surveying demands a remarkable degree of devotion to duty and the area covered, unless a mere outline is the objective, is unlikely to be very large. Expeditions committed to surveying at sea or requiring accurate detailed maps of areas in which they are operating, use aerial photographs for the production of their maps. Both hot air balloons and radio controlled model aircraft are possibilities but the latter are much more flexible. Suitable model seaplanes can easily be launched by hand from a boat and retrieved with ease so long as the sea is not too rough. This technique, however, obviously requires that the boat is kept in the camera's field so that there is an object of known size on the photographs to allow for their being adjusted to a common scale in the enlarger.

In the gathering darkness across a jagged reef, covered by only about a metre of water but so full of holes that we were constantly falling, pushing ashore our Honda suitcase-style generator on a polystyrene flotation pallet, team members could be excused for wondering about the indispensability of some of the items of equipment which we had taken to some of the most unlikely spots in the Red Sea. But the generator was essential for charging batteries for the cine camera and underwater lights. In other words, as our plans got more ambitious our equipment necessarily got heavier, more expensive and needed more professional attention. Nevertheless, for long periods in the field the generator and refrigerator that I often humped around to keep my films in good order were much appreciated for rather more direct reasons—apart from their obvious uses for lighting and making ice, a refrigerator does offer a means of keeping fish fresh. In order to avoid noise at night, we used, when on an island or ashore, to site the generator on the end of about 75 metres of cable in a convenient depression or behind a rocky outcrop. Under more confined conditions at sea, we would run the generator at intervals during the day: with lower night temperatures the contents of the refrigerator would normally survive fairly well until morning without it being started.

Much could be said on the available models of refrigerators, generators and compressors. As a general rule, it is better not to proliferate the number of fuels in use: paraffin refrigerators may be cheap to run but they do tend to blow out in windy conditions. What is essential is to match the generator to the refrigerator as the initial surge current requirement of the latter is high. Cooking over gas is probably the most convenient though a paraffin Primus is equally useful. It cannot be over emphasized that with both systems there are dangers. An accidental flare up in a small boat is horrifying. I once lost my eyelashes and almost the boat when, confident that I had effected a perfect Araldite repair to a gas junction, I tested the result with a lighted match!

With aqualung cylinders the pattern of valve is very much a

matter of individual choice, but for expedition use it is as well to go for real comfort when using one for long periods at a time. Whichever pattern is selected it is important that water is kept out of the HP side when washing salt off the valve, and a pressure gauge in my view verges on being a necessity, unless the cylinder has a reserve and lever. The condition of aqualung cylinders is more important than their type or metal. Don't ever risk your own and your companions' lives with a rusted cylinder, and, in particular, don't do so where temperatures are so high that pressures rise almost unnoticed to very high figures. Be careful not to bang cylinders against fixed obstructions. Ideally the harness should be of soft cloth webbing which is very comfortable over bare skin; regrettably most available commercial harnesses today are made of synthetic webbing which is much harsher. Whatever the manuals say don't feel obliged to wear the aqualung crotch strap when diving for long under water. It is hardly even necessary for the comfortable positioning of the cylinder on your back and you thus avoid the discomfort the strap causes when you are not wearing a suit.

The future of underwater exploration on the scientific front can be seen as an extension of its present role. This is usually information gathering, but it can be either professional or amateur or—as is perhaps most common—a mixture of the two. Animal behaviour is an obvious field for enquiry. Our extensive activities in the Red Sea and Indian Ocean over eight years and involving nearly seventy-five expedition members from post-doctoral to undergraduate, all concerned with the Crown of Thorns starfish *Acanthster planci* perhaps amount to one of the more remarkable demonstrations of the role of the scientific underwater expedition.

It takes no particular foresight to see a pattern emerging. Given a central nucleus with an overall project and appropriate laboratory facilities, there is a very definite role for supporting scientific expeditions. The formula however only works really well when senior scientists with appropriate qualifications are available to brief and participate in the supporting expeditionary parties. Occasionally, and especially with collecting expeditions, it is unnecessary for the team to include anyone with post-graduate scientific qualifications but it is essential that the briefing should be of high quality. It must be obvious that there is a high risk of an expensive expeditionary venture not being capitalized to its maximum extent when no one involved has the knowledge necessary to recognize lateral or tangental opportunities for new and worthwhile research.

With growing world wide concern over pollution in innumerable and often very subtle forms, it becomes more necessary to be able to identify deviations from the norm. In our central research programme at the Cambridge Coral Starfish Research Group we became deeply involved in studying an animal, *A. planci*, which happened to prove to be a very sensitive indicator of environmental changes. As such it deserves to be monitored as a form of early warning against possible pollution pressure on the environment. Research is needed to identify more of the marine species which react early and significantly to changes in the environment and especially ones of a chemical nature. Since this form of environment safeguarding can be implemented, through expeditions, by those with only basic training and inexpensive equipment, it should be possible to apply extensively the information yielded by the progress of research. Many areas of the world's oceans and seas which have islands and reefs have either no, or only a very small, indigenous population. In these areas especially there will be a developing role for expeditions. For those expeditions with greater relevant scientific qualification in their membership, base line studies of a more general kind must also be important. There is an enormous distance to go in completing known base line surveys over the world's seas and there is general agreement that pollution can best be recognized when deviations from an original base line study or survey can be established by straightforward reference and comparison.

Another area for valid and valuable underwater expeditionary activity is that of the general search for marine organisms which will yield significant pharmaceuticals. All manner of drugs, herbicides, pesticides and many other biochemical and chemical products are potentially to be found in marine organisms. During 1974 our Research Group was working, through an expedition structure, on an intensive sampling of the potential of the central Red Sea: ICI were our partners in this investigation and expected to spend many months screening the first hundred samples we had collected. With regional variations in marine fauna as extensive as they are, and with the varying conditions of the organisms themselves—for example, in and out of breeding conditions—it is readily apparent that this field of investigation, so long as there are sufficient pharmaceutical companies still interested, will take years to exhaust.

Whoever plans and leads an underwater expedition can never forget the experience. Whoever participates in one should never forget it. Not because it is modish, not because it is the obvious complement to terrestrial experience but because the sea is the last of the vast unknowns.

"....RATHER THAN TO HOPE THAT DIVERS CAN BECOME SCIENTISTS"

7. OCEAN SAILING

by Chay Blyth

Earlier this year I was addressing an international conference of two thousand businessmen in Nice. The theme of the week-long seminar was 'The Will to Win', and I was one of the guest speakers. The chairman of the conference, the man who actually had to introduce me to the delegates, had done his homework. He mentioned rowing the Atlantic, sailing round the world in *British Steel*, and the achievements of our paratrooper team in the global sailing race. Then, as I was beginning to cringe with the embarrassment that always wells up in me on such occasions, the chairman continued: 'But of course, Chay is not always a winner. There was a time when, as a brash young man who knew next to nothing about sailing a yacht, he entered the Golden Globe Round the World Race. He borrowed a boat and set out with only a few hours of solo sailing behind him. What's more he openly boasted to the newspapers that he would win the race.

'Well, he didn't win. True, he was leading as the race competitors rounded Cape Horn but soon afterwards he had to make landfall in South Africa. I hope therefore that when Chay tells us about his adventures he gives us the reasons for failure as well as success.'

It was a well-made point and, incidentally, helped me to establish an immediate rapport with the audience who so often hear such a eulogistic introduction that they sit with bated breath waiting for a bionic man to appear. Amidst the volume of praise that inevitably accompanies success it is often easy and convenient to forget failure. I try never to forget it because I believe that setbacks and abortive efforts are all part of the pattern of achievement.

The sensible man will learn by his mistakes and the overwhelming lesson I received from my first vain attempt to sail around the world (I broached eleven times in succession in the yacht *Dytiscus*) was that preparation is 90 per cent of the job. It was instilled into me during my Army career and I have taken care to remember it since I returned to civvy street. The only time that I forgot the lesson and felt I could beat the system was when I sailed *Dytiscus* and that ended in disaster.

My taste for adventure and exploration was prompted by my time in the Army. The Forces have their faults but to my mind there is no finer training ground for a young man and certainly the opportunities are there for the taking. That popular misconception about 'never volunteer' in the Army could not in fact be further from the truth. If I fancied a job I put my name down for it, and that way I saw Aden, Cyprus, learned how to use a gun, swim, canoe, and survive. When John Ridgway was looking for someone to row the Atlantic with him I offered to go along for the ride, and look how that changed my life. Here again though, preparation was all important. We trained meticulously, running for hours each day with full kit. Rations were equally carefully planned and we worked out our calorie requirement precisely because we knew that we had to pull every ounce of weight in that boat one hell of a long way. The efficiency of our planning ensured our success. At the start we were just two human beings no more suited than the next two men to row a little boat on a big sea but we made ourselves better by tuning our bodies and making sure we had the right tools for the job.

After the row in 1966 we were subjected to all the hullabaloo that swirls around paper heroes and stupidly I began to believe just a pinch of what I read about myself. Fatal. He who believes his own publicity is heading for a fall, yet I am sure it is one of the biggest pitfalls associated with any activity which focuses attention on a person. The theatre, politics, films, so much drivel is written about the personalities involved that it is a constant source of amazement to me that readers continue to believe it.

And when the subjects themselves think the words are true there is no hope.

It was in a mood of euphoria therefore that I entered *Dytiscus* in the Golden Globe race. A friend had loaned me the yacht and I had about five hours' tuition before setting off. Although I did my best as far as provisions, navigation, spares, and the dozen-and-one things that have to be thought about are concerned, it was a foolhardy attempt. Only luck got me as far as South Africa. A bad workman blames his tools but the fact is that I had not got the right yacht for the job and there was the added hazard that when it came to experience I was as green as grass.

When I came back to Britain I was a wiser and saner man. I had learned several lessons in addition to the preparation imprint. For instance I knew that determination was not enough, and also that to boast beforehand makes failure all the more painful. I had discovered that I did not know it all, in fact I knew very little, and that my knowledge had to be much broader before I undertook a major adventure again. Nevertheless my desire for challenge had been sharpened by the experience and it was while my wife Maureen and I were sailing *Dytiscus* back from the Azores that the idea of a circumnavigation westwards was born. It was Maureen's idea, germinated as we sunned ourselves on the deck thinking of 'things that have never been done before'. My thoughts were fanciful—parachute into the forests at the source of the Amazon then walk to the coast; walk across the Australian desert; try a single-handed trip to the South Pole. Maureen's notion seemed the most feasible so when I returned to Britain I determined to investigate it further. This time there was to be no half-hearted effort. I determined that my preparations would be meticulous and that is a maxim that has served me well ever since.

The story of *British Steel* and my voyage around the world has already been well chronicled (*The Impossible Voyage*, published by Hodder & Stoughton). Actually the phrase 'single handed' is a misnomer because although I did the sailing the whole venture was a team effort involving Maureen, the designer Robert Clark, the builders Philip & Son, the British Steel Corporation, and a host of good friends. Without them the achievement would truly have been an impossibility.

I planned the whole thing very carefully. I talked with experts, drove the length and breadth of the country to obtain the right equipment, took a crash course in everything from first aid to using a television camera, counted calories, cajoled sponsors, fought frustrations and hardly slept. I gave up my job and I sold our house because make no mistake the only way to succeed in a venture like this is to make it take precedence over everything else. It becomes a passion, a fixation, over-riding every other consideration. I realize it is a selfish attitude and I cannot explain its origins in me, but it is the only way. It is so easy to accept excuses for non-delivery, to listen sympathetically to hard luck stories from suppliers, to accept postponement. My belief is that once your target is established nothing, but nothing, should interfere with its attainment.

Fortunately the criticisms of others have never bothered me. According to the pundits the voyage of *British Steel* was foolhardy, ill-advised and doomed. I don't blame them, they did not know how careful my planning was and anyway they are paid to spread gloom and despondency. All of them are quick to say 'I told you so' but those I respect are the chaps who are prepared to admit they were wrong.

British Steel is a 59-foot ketch that was designed to sail around the world against the prevailing winds and tides. The efficiency of the design and construction is shown by the fact that she did the job and did it well. Since the completion of the voyage she has been converted to a twelve berth yacht and has sailed around the world again with her name changed to *British Soldier* and with an all-Army crew. She was also the first British boat home in the 1972 Trans-Atlantic Race (my friend Brian Cooke, who was later tragically lost from his trimaran, was at the helm) and took part in the French-sponsored Atlantic Triangle Race. Altogether

British Steel has sailed more than 100,000 sea miles in five years which must be something of a yachting record.

The news that there was to be a round-the-world race for crewed yachts really fired my imagination. I heard about it while I was on my *British Steel* voyage and immediately I began to make plans. I wanted a big yacht, a ketch, and I wanted to sail it my way. The crew would have to be hand picked, not for their sailing experience but for their ability to take and understand orders; their initiative under stress; their desire to learn. When the *British Steel* ballyhoo had died down I set about achieving this new target and once again it became the most important thing in my life. It is this journey that I want to consider in this chapter because I think it illustrates well the involvements of a major sailing expedition.

First, as Mrs Beeton is often quoted as saying, you should catch your rabbit. In my case the rabbit was a yacht and I knew that if we were to win the race it would be a very expensive yacht. Fresh from my *British Steel* success I set about tackling the biggest threat to any venture, sponsorship. Cigarette companies have whole departments devoted to writing 'Sorry, but we cannot help you' letters and every day dozens of letters arrive on the doorsteps of banks, breweries, soap powder manufacturers, and so on all asking for financial backing for schemes. If there is a secret for sponsorship seekers it is that sponsors should always be told what is in it for them. No use telling the chairman of 'Sch . . . You Know Who' what a fine sailor you are and how a 25.5 metre ketch in GRP will conform to the RNSA rules if the man has never been on a boat in his life. You might as well be discussing moon walks. But if you explain how your venture could fit in with his overall marketing policies, how you have a tie-up with the *Daily Globe* newspaper and that television will be producing an hour-long documentary on your activities, then he can understand the proposition.

In my case I had convinced an international petrol company that the sponsoring of a yacht would be valuable publicity for them. All systems were 'go' when the Middle East oil crisis blew up, budgets were cut, and my new yacht became a dream again. It was here that the slice of luck without which one cannot operate came into play. While on a brief visit to the Bahamas I met that remarkable British patriot 'Union Jack' Hayward. He listened to my plans and a few days later quite out of the blue, rang up to say he would finance the building of the new yacht. There were no contracts, nothing in writing, but I was soon to learn that Jack's word was better than any bit of paper. With his backing we were able to build the yacht *Great Britain II*, appropriately named after Brunel's iron ship *SS Great Britain* which Jack had paid for to come back from the Falklands to Britain. Her Royal Highness The Princess Anne graciously agreed to launch the yacht so we had the finest boat and the very best patronage.

Now to the crew. Remember I said they had to be bright, responsive to orders, and reliable. There is only one body of men I know from personal experience that possesses these qualities. I had been a paratrooper, knew how they operated and the kind of men the regiment bred. The Army agreed to ask for volunteers and we were inundated. Almost three hundred men put their names down as possible crew and we were faced with the task of sorting the wheat from the chaff. It was impossible to interview them all so my initial selection was crude but effective. I called impromptu meetings at awkward times. The venue was usually difficult to reach and the meeting invariably coincided with a mealtime. Anyone who did not turn up was automatically excluded from the possibles and no excuses were accepted. The system may seem hard but it was expedient. Personal interviews followed and I ended up with twenty potential crew members for *Great Britain II*.

Only three of the men had ever sailed before and only two had been on board a big yacht. That did not concern me too much because they were all willing to be trained. My aim was to weld the men into a team, evaluating the strengths and weaknesses before making my final selection. We lived together for weeks and I evolved a programme designed to test them almost to breaking point.

The culmination of this period was reached when we went up to my cottage in Scotland for a fortnight of intensive training. It is a two-up-and-two-down cottage with cold running water on the edge of a forest. The nearest house to it is four miles away and the nearest road the same distance. At the end of the fortnight I had to make my selection so the men knew that this was the finale. On my part I made the whole exercise as difficult and uncomfortable as possible. Each man was given a small area in one of the bedrooms for his bed and personal belongings. Every morning each bed had to be broken down and stacked neatly in the tiny space. If there was so much as a blanket corner hanging over the designated area the owner knew he would be expelled from the team.

Every day we had lectures and discussions on various aspects of sailing or current affairs. Men who had never given a talk in their lives were suddenly asked to extol the virtues of the sextant or describe the wind variations in the Southern Ocean. We discussed such emotive subjects as Ireland, where many of our friends and colleagues had been killed, and sex. I provoked arguments and needled men until they almost came to blows because we were going to spend eight months together in the restricted environment of a yacht and compatibility was going to be a prime consideration.

Of course the Scottish test had its lighter moments. We had to get up every morning at six o'clock and go for a five-mile run with full kit before breakfast. There was a rule that we were not allowed to speak to outsiders for any reason whatsoever so I shudder to think what the bewildered postman must have thought as twenty sweating men with heavy packs on their backs studiously ignored his cheerful 'Good morning' as they ran past him.

I deliberately kept the evenings free because I wanted to test the reaction to boredom. It was dark, there were no newspapers, no television, no radio. On the third night Pete Bates, a tall tough man with a laconic sense of humour, suddenly put down the book he was reading in his bedroom and got dressed in his best suit. Carefully he straightened his tie and smoothed his hair down. 'Where the hell are you going?' asked one of his room-mates because it was against the rules to go out after dark.

'I'm going to have a night out,' said Pete. 'I am going to visit Len in the next bedroom and ask him if he would care to join me in a game of cards.' He meant it too, and so successful was the visit that the next night Len put on his Sunday best and went visiting Pete!

By the end of a week I had made my selection. There were some men who obviously did not fit in and who were not going to make the final crew. I do not believe in postponing such decisions once my mind is made up so I told the unlucky few who were not going to be included in future plans. They all took the news well except one chap who told me where I could put my yacht and threatened to smash my face. I told him that while I admired such courage the yacht would not fit and the question of who would smash whose face was debatable. I'm pleased to say it all ended amicably.

I was down to a dozen, all tough men and keen as a razor. The snag was that most of them had never sailed before and this problem caused me to lose one more of the complement. We had a week's training at the Sea Survival School, run by the Navy, and one of the exercises was to be tipped into the water, right an upturned dinghy, and paddle to safety. In big seas it is rather a complex exercise but as it is carried out under strict supervision there is little danger. One of my men was in a complete stupor. He did not obey orders, sat rigid in the dinghy, and was absolutely petrified. It was so foreign to his nature and to my previous knowledge of him that I did not get angry even when we were safely ashore. 'Sorry, boss,' he said. 'I don't know what came over me. When I got near the water I just went numb.'

12. *Second Life* during the Round the World Yacht Race of 1973.

Training had taught me that people do suffer with phobias and this crewman was frightened of the sea as some folk are of heights or enclosed spaces. He had not known the fear before simply because he had not been that close to the water. Regretfully I had to tell him he was not wanted on the voyage.

The final test for crew selection involved personal interviews with a lady psychiatrist. She asked a series of questions designed to test our compatibility, and our ability to cope under stress. All the chaps, with just two exceptions, came out of the tests with flying colours. As one of those who failed was me I decided to disregard the results!

You may wonder why I went to all this trouble to choose my crew and why I opted for character rather than sailing ability. You would not pose the question if you had seen the dissent among the crews of other yachts in the race. The French and the Italians in particular were vitriolic (with the notable exception of

Eric Tabarly who as always ran a disciplined ship). Naturally we had our differences on board *Great Britain II* but they were relatively minor and I'm afraid I cannot tell you about them—one of the rules was that no one, not even me, was allowed to talk or write about personal relationships on board.

In retrospect it is possible that I sacrificed too much sail training in my efforts to select a crew. The result was that when the race started we were not working as a perfect team and we did not do particularly well on the first leg to Cape Town. By the second leg we were going well and on the final two stretches there was no yacht to touch us. I am sure that given the same crew again, with the experience we have obtained, we could crack any circumnavigation record.

Shortly after the successful Bonington Everest expedition I watched a television documentary in which Chris said that on a task of that magnitude there had to be one final person in command. Group discussion is valuable and everyone should be entitled to an opinion on decisions, but in the end there can only be one decision maker. I agree with Chris completely. On my yacht there is one skipper, me, although I am happy to delegate routine responsibility.

My Army training taught me that neatness is a great morale booster. There is a temptation when faced with a long period at sea among all-male company to become scruffy in personal appearance and to leave the tidying up to someone else. This makes for an inefficient and potentially dangerous yacht because if everything is not in its place there is the possibility of a delay in finding something when speed may be vital. Therefore I insist that my yachts are kept tidy at all times, that sails are cared for and stowed immediately rather than left lying about the deck. And when we approach a port I demand a special 'bull' session, decks are scrubbed and maybe painted, teak is oiled, stainless steel is polished. I insist too that any half-hearted attempts at beards or moustaches are shaved away and hair is cut. Whenever *Great Britain II* reached land the crew were dressed in identical uniform, usually special orange sweaters and blue flannels. No matter how bad that leg of the voyage had been our yacht was immaculate when we tied up. I have learned that presentation is important and a little bit of effort in that direction makes a great deal of difference. I do not mean to be brash, in fact it is essential to be modest, but you owe it to your yacht, your crew, your sponsor and yourself to appear at your best when the eyes of the publicity media are upon you.

When budgets are tight (and with most ventures they are) there is a tendency to write letters to all and sundry asking for goods and equipment free of charge. Commendably many firms co-operate but there is a hidden danger in their generosity. The temptation is to take equipment that is not quite right for the job because it is free issue whereas the company producing exactly the right tool for the job wants to charge you for its product. Compromise for economy is a philosophy I will not accept unless it is absolutely necessary. On my yachts I want Ratsey and Lapthorne sails and Brookes and Gatehouse electrics, Ford or Perkins engines and Lewmar winches. Nothing less is acceptable.

Naturally every venture I tackle has its peculiarities but I have evolved Ten Commandments which I stick to and which should help others:

1. Listen to experts but do not necessarily accept what they say.
2. Plan carefully.
3. Get the right equipment.
4. Have a good team to support you.
5. Be completely dedicated to the project.
6. Be efficient.
7. Learn from mistakes.
8. Train properly.
9. Make your own decisions.
10. Never believe your own publicity.

8. RIVER AND WHITE WATER EXPLORATION

by Roger Chapman

INTRODUCTION

'. . . We slip smoothly down the tongue of the rapids in our small Avon inflatable—suddenly we're in seething waves—sensation of being bounced like a rubber ball—huge wall of brown water immediately in front of us—"we can't get through that"—the craft is skewing sideways—water everywhere—the brown wall has gone—rushing down towards a hydraulic wave—we've lost control of the craft—body and mind completely numbed by excitement—"Oh! Christ I'm being thrown out"—no, just tossed up as the rear end kicks up—Chris and Ian are still there—and suddenly we know we're through it. . . . the tension bursts like a bubble, and on the rocks by the side of the river there is talk and laughter.'

This short extract from the diary of a member of the Blue Nile (Great Abbai) Expedition in 1968—experiencing the first major rapids just below Lake Tana in Ethiopia—illustrates the tremendous exhilaration of white water expeditioning. There is something unique about that close companionship, that dependence on a reliable inflated craft and that intensity of living experienced in putting one's skills against the power and magnificence of a great river.

Today, particularly in the United States, river running has become a national sport. The skills and techniques of white water rafting and canoeing have improved immeasurably since that expedition in 1968, by men who had made a career of running such rivers as the Colorado through the Grand Canyon, the Snake through Hell's Canyon, the St. John, St. Croix and Fraser River. Now, it is possible for holiday trippers, using these techniques, to travel safely through some of the most stunning scenery in the world.

But the excitement and thrills should not detract the would-be expeditioner from realizing the main purpose of a river; providing a route through the inaccessible parts of the interior.

As geographic exploration ends, scientific exploration is gaining momentum. Today it is the scientists who wish to carry out research projects in remote parts of the world where there are no roads or railways, only rivers which form a constant highway. For this reason, river expeditions through remote countries are increasing in number, but many of the members of such trips have little or no experience of handling boats safely through rapids and cataracts. There are no rivers in the United Kingdom, on which they can train and practise, which can compare with the power, ferocity and treacherous currents of the great rivers of America, Africa or the Asian Continent, where often millions of tons of wild water cascade through gorges, down rapids and plunge over waterfalls or cataracts as the rivers cut their way through the mountainous wilderness towards the plains and the calm estuaries which lead to the oceans.

The first part of this chapter is designed to assist expeditions who are intending to take rubber inflatable craft, which can carry all the scientific and camping equipment for a period of a couple of months, down youthful rivers. It will advise how to negotiate some of the hazards caused by rapids, cataracts, bends and boulders along the route. The second part of the chapter is designed for the canoeist who is running the river for the sheer excitement and fun. Yet the principles and rules of handling craft in white water remain the same both for the explorer and the adventurer if he or she is to complete the journey with skill and safety. . . .

YOUTHFUL RIVERS—RAPIDS AND CATARACTS

Any river of magnitude has its source in hills or mountains where rainfall continually feeds it with runoff waters organized into drainage systems. Carrying debris in their wake, these youthful streams are initially guided downwards through depressions in the land form. Later, as they pick up speed and volume, they cut through the rock of the mountains forming steep-walled gorges or canyons through which the rapids gush, and smooth down the lips of waterfalls, turning them into step-like cataracts. Eventually, as the river emerges from the hills and reaches the plains of the coastal belt, it begins to slow down, meanders and broadens, before eventually entering the estuary mouth which opens to the sea.

Many lives have been lost in the early exploration of great continents by men using wooden boats to navigate such rapids and cataracts. Many rivers still remain unnavigated.

As scientific exploration continues, and man seeks knowledge of the rocks, minerals, hydrology and hydro electrical power within such gorges or canyons, techniques have been evolved to descend safely down these turbulent white waters. In the last fifteen years these techniques have improved considerably as a result of men studying in great detail the rivers of North America with the aim of promoting river running as a sport and recreation.

The speed of the water flowing through rapids is caused by the *gradient* or slope of the river bed—the steeper the river bed the faster the water; the *turbulence* is caused by the rocks, boulders and ledges under the water and the bottle-necks within the gorge; whilst the *volume* of water is swelled by precipitation (rainfall) or ablation (melting snow) in springtime. Spring runoff, as it is called, can turn mild rivers running at 3 knots into raging torrents, crashing over boulders and racing through gorges at speeds of up to 12 knots or more.

THE TONGUE OR V

As a result of water flowing faster in the centre or deeper part of a river, the river takes on distinct characteristics when entering a rapid. The current creates a smooth tongue of fast flowing water which, from the air, looks like a V pointing down stream. The obstacles near the start of rapids cause the water along the flanks to slow down and form a distinct white line in the shape of a tongue. In most cases, this V-shaped tongue marks out the best point of entry into a rapid.

STANDING WAVES/HAYSTACKS

When the current, which has been flowing down a smooth slope into the rapids, suddenly hits an obstacle or slow water, caused by the slope flattening out, there are a series of large *standing waves* in a fixed position at the tip of the tongue shaped like great mounds or haystacks. These waves can be anything up to ten feet high and when capped in foam it is wise to avoid them by steering to the left or right. If they are smooth or rounded it is possible to float right over them by keeping the bows straight into the waves. On the crest of the first mound, the others can be seen stretching for up to a hundred yards or more, with each succeeding wave getting smaller and closer together until eventually they disappear.

STOPPER WAVE

One of the most common types of turbulence in cataracts—step-like drops or vertical falls—is called a *stopper* and is caused by water plunging over a ledge and forming a relatively stationary, but powerful, wave at the foot. Unfortunately such turbulences are extremely difficult to detect from a craft in the water and the only sure way to predict them is during a foot reconnaissance down the bank. They frequently look deceptively easy to negotiate but they must be avoided at all costs as the back current can easily flip a craft and possibly drown the crew who may be kept turning under water by the power of the vortex. Most river runners who have experienced a flip in a stopper will never forget the feeling of complete helplessness as the river continues to drag them down and around, lifejacket and all, until it eventually regurgitates them a hundred yards or so further down the rapids. So, never attempt to navigate a vertical drop unless there is at least a 45° slope of water and plenty of run out below. If you are unable to avoid it by manoeuvring round the flanks it is wise to line the craft unmanned over the drop with ropes, then re-embark well clear of the surface back flow.

REVERSALS/HOLES

The most frequent type of turbulence in rapids is the *reversal* caused by the surface backflow just beyond a submerged rock or boulder. It should be avoided whenever possible, but, if by chance, because of lack of foot reconnaissance the craft slides over the submerged boulder into the reversal, the oarsman and paddlers must dig deeply into the forward moving water to drive the craft through as fast as possible. Otherwise it will spin, swamp or, at worst, flip over.

EDDIES

The main location of an eddy is just beyond an outjutting section of the bank and is a part of the river where the current stops or flows upstream. The stronger the current the more intense the eddy which often circles slowly. In the centre of rapids eddies formed behind jutting rocks or midstream boulders can prove to be handy stopping places to bale out water, to have a rest or to plan the tactics for tackling the next stretch of white water.

EDDIES

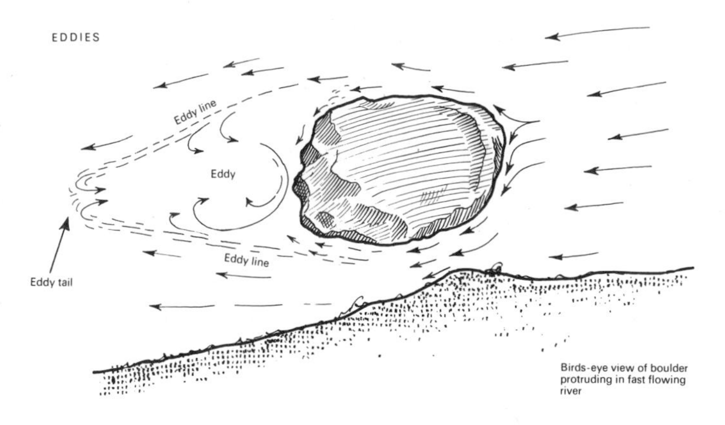

Birds-eye view of boulder protruding in fast flowing river

BENDS

As a result of centrifugal force, the water on a bend is drawn towards the outside bank where it often crashes against rocks before ricocheting into the centre of the river again. The danger of this is obvious, so crews should attempt to take their craft along the inside bank and get round the corner before the current drives them across the river into turbulent water. A good entry close to the inside bank and a cautious approach is vital so that the skipper can have a good look around the corner for obstacles, stoppers or reversals.

SHALLOWS

When the river broadens as it approaches the plains and estuaries it will become shallow and expose many more rocks. Often a member of the crew must stand up in the craft and direct the oarsmen or steer along the best channels to avoid grounding on shingle or wedging the boat amid exposed boulders. If the inflatable craft at this stage is fitted with an outboard motor, great care must be taken to avoid damaging the propeller. A man should be positioned in the bows with the sole task of observing the depth of the water and shouting a warning to the helmsman when to lift the engine.

RECONNAISSANCE

There is an old Army adage: 'Time spent on reconnaissance is never wasted.' When you have the responsibility of the lives of the crew of your craft on your hands then this can never be over emphasized. Do not trust anyone else's reconnaissance of a river or an aerial reconnaissance. The power of the water and the height of vertical drops cannot be accurately ascertained from an aeroplane. The river may well have risen in height since someone else's reconnaissance report. There is only one way to do it. If you are the leader, *you* must walk or rock-hop down the banks of the rapids noting all the obstacles, reversals, stoppers and standing waves. It takes time to read water and judge the best route through the rapids. If it helps, draw a rough diagram on a piece of paper and discuss the best route through the rapids with the other skippers. Do not miss out any portion, because in the stretch you have missed there may be a small waterfall which could cause that fatal accident which may mean abandoning your expedition.

This is where the real skill of the white water runner is tested.

The crucial decision on how to tackle the problem now has to be made:

Firstly, should the craft be portaged round the rapids?
Secondly, should the craft be lined with rope down the bank?
Thirdly, if the rapid is navigable then plan the run through the rapids on the simplest and most direct route.

Once you have made your decision, you return to the crew who will be waiting patiently in the craft. Give your briefing and final instructions. Check all the equipment is secure and tighten the straps. Check everyone is wearing lifejackets, crash helmets and gym shoes and is in his correct position in the craft. Push off from the bank. Your test is about to begin.

Once over the lip and into the tongue of the rapid there is no turning back. . . .

EQUIPMENT

THE IDEAL INFLATABLE CRAFT

The inflatables used on extended expeditions naturally vary with the size of the river, the number of members and the equipment required to be carried. Generally, the choice of size varies from 4 to 6 metres long and 2 to 3 metres wide because this is a size which is easily portable on land both inflated and deflated, and is big enough to negotiate the fiercest rapids. Recently, giant inflatable rafts—similar to those used by the Colorado River runners—were used on the Zaïre River to transport tons of equipment and large numbers of expedition members on this scientific venture, but this type of giant craft will only be mentioned briefly as they are rarely used on expeditions because of the high cost of transportation to and from the river.

SMALL INFLATABLES

Avon Inflatables Ltd., of Llanelli, Wales, are the foremost makers in the world of inflatable craft for river expeditions. Since three modified Avon *Redshanks* (3.73 metres by 1.68 metres) navigated the Blue Nile in 1968, they have experimented and produced larger and more durable craft. The *Adventurer* (4 metres by 2 metres), the *Professional* (4.57 metres by 2.24 metres) and the *Spirit* (5.33 metres by 2.43 metres) have been built especially for river running and river expeditions.

Many lessons were learnt as a result of the Blue Nile Expedition about the construction and modifications needed, as it was not only sharp rocks this expedition had to contend with but also crocodiles and hippopotamuses whose teeth can puncture even the toughest nylon-Hypalon fabric. Separated air compartments, valves large enough to insert and then inflate football bladders in the tubes, lengthened painters on the bow and stern, secured D-rings, lifelines outside and inside the craft, hand holds along the strengthened bottom underneath the craft, raised bows, and thwarts fitted with waterproof zips to improve storage space, are just some of the modifications which can make the Avons one of the most durable and safest craft on the river.

One of the greatest problems with the Avon *Redshank* in the large rapids of the Blue Nile was swamping, making the craft so heavy and sluggish that it was almost impossible to manoeuvre the craft away from the more dangerous parts of the river. As a result, Avons developed much larger tubes in later models—the *Professional* with 51 cm tubes and the *Spirit* with 53 cm tubes, making these two the ideal craft to choose for extended journeys down some of the largest rivers in the world.

GIANT INFLATABLES

On the Zaïre River giant 12 metre inflatable craft were fitted with enormous tubes called sponsons lashed to each side of the boat

Review Copy

EXPEDITIONS: The Expert's Way
Ed. by John Blashford-Snell and
Alistair Ballantine.
(Faber Paperbacks)

Publication date:
16th May, 1977 at £2.60
NB. A Cloth Edtn. is also avail. at
£4.95

No review should appear before the date of publication.
Photographs and biographical notes of authors are usually available and will be supplied on request to the Reviews Department.
Use of illustration material can also be arranged.

Faber & Faber

3 QUEEN SQUARE LONDON WC1N 3AU
Telephone: 01-278 6881

for stability. These giant 'pontoons' were driven by a 40 horse-power engine mounted on a transom just inside the stern with an extra 40 horse-power engine as reserve fitted in the centre of the craft.

These formidable load carriers held between fifteen and twenty-five members of the expedition and nearly a ton of petrol, food and equipment sufficient for a period of five days before re-supply. The technique of handling these craft in turbulent waters has been mastered by American tour operators taking holiday parties through the Grand Canyon down the Colorado River where they often raft three of these enormous boats together to negotiate the worst of the rapids.

EQUIPMENT FOR USE WITH SMALLER INFLATABLES

Rowing frame

The Americans have refined the technique of taking smaller 4 to 6 metre craft with these giant inflatables through the Grand Canyon. They have constructed and introduced rowing-frames mounted on top of the tubes from where an oarsman can row the boat safely through the worst of the cataracts.

On the Blue Nile the Avon *Redshanks* were propelled by two paddlers in the front compartment with the skipper or helmsman steering the craft in the rear by trailing a large paddle as a rudder over the stern. Although this method proved reasonably successful, tremendous effort was required to get enough forward motion in the larger rapids to make steering effective. If the *Redshanks* were swamped with water, it proved almost impossible to steer them effectively. With the rowing-frame the Avon inflatables can be controlled and steered by a simple pair of oars. The frame also offers an elevated seat for the skipper/oarsman in order that he can read the water well ahead.

The frame mounted on top of the tubes holds a decking, by chains, off the bottom of the craft allowing it to slide easily across

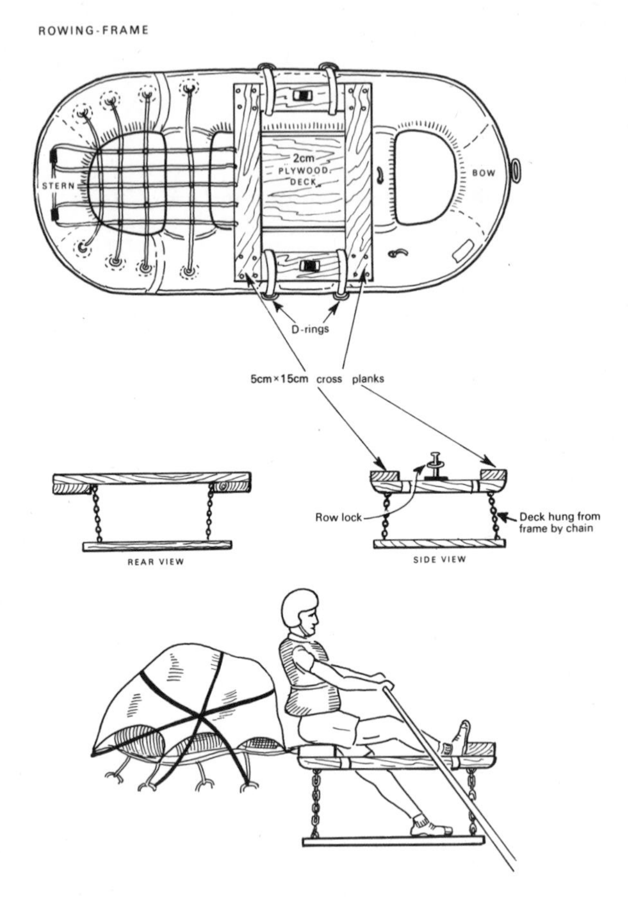

shallows and submerged rocks, reducing the wear and tear on the hull and giving the oarsman a firm floor.

As the craft can be manoeuvred safely by one skilled oarsman he can take a group of inexperienced beginners through some of the most exciting water.

Oars

All oars should be made of a hardwood, such as ash or maple, which has a slight give yet is strong enough to withstand

WOODEN OAR WITH FIBRE GLASS COVERED TIP

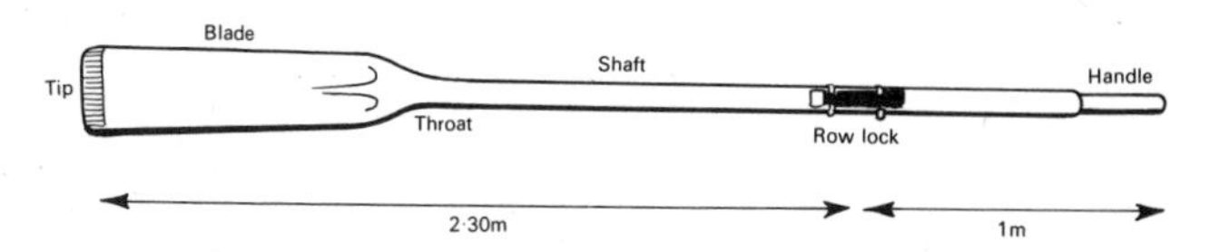

battering and the ferocious power of white water. For the smaller craft between 4 and 5.5 metres, the oars should be about 3 metres in length and be fibreglassed at the tip of the blades.

It is inadvisable to use the light oars often issued with the Avon craft as they are only designed for rowing across a calm harbour and will easily snap under pressure, as do the 3 metre ash oars if caught or wedged in rocks. You should also take a couple of spare oars aboard the craft, stowed in a position which is easily accessible for immediate use.

Rowlocks

In the past most expeditions have used the circular swivel ring rowlock so that the oar will not pop out of its mounting when being rowed through a turbulent patch of water, but recently the

THOLE PIN MOUNT AND ROW LOCK

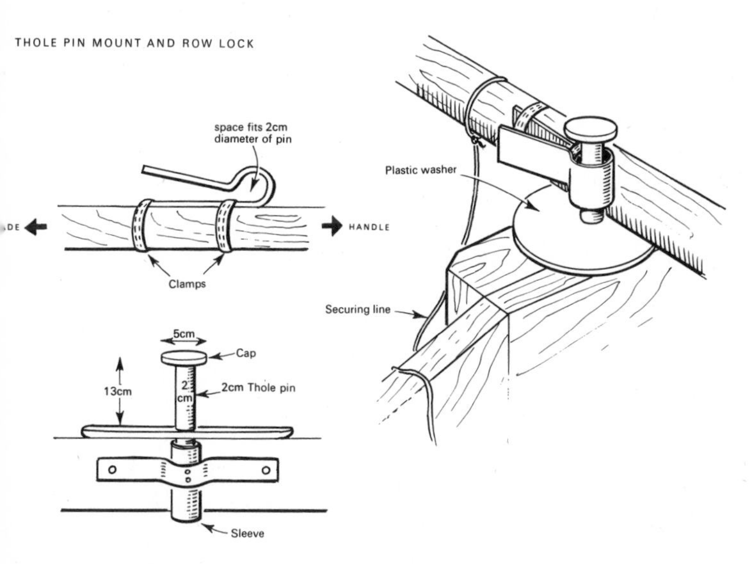

Americans have introduced an ingenious new rowlock which ensures the oar blades are continuously vertical.

Paddles

Even when the small inflatable has an experienced oarsman aboard, the remaining members of the crew can assist by providing paddle power at the bows and stern. If a paddle has a fibreglass covered tip, it can be used to ward off boulders and rocks on the journey through the rapids.

The paddle should vary in length between 1.65 metres and 2 metres depending on the size and strength of the paddler. However, the skipper or helmsman at the rear of the craft should have a 3.15 metre paddle so that he can get more leverage on his steering strokes.

Engines

Although the sport of white water running precludes the use of motors, outboard engines are invaluable on extended expeditions when there are long stretches of calm waters between cataracts and broad, smooth, meandering runs near the mouth of the river. Even the fastest stretch of water travels at a speed of no more than 12 to 16 knots, thus an engine is essential over long periods when the river is travelling slowly. Avons have produced the S400 with a transom to carry up to a 40 hp engine, making it an ideal craft to use for fast reconnaissance in large rapids to select the best route for giant inflatables to follow. The *Adventurer* is also fitted with rubber brackets so that a transom for a 26 hp engine can be mounted. The *Professional* and *Spirit* are not modified for engines unless requested.

One of the best and most tried engines in white water is the *Mercury* which has been used on several large expeditions because of its reliability. However, the problem with carrying engines is that an adequate supply of petrol and oil has to be brought overland by a support group to a pre-arranged rendezvous on the river bank. If this is possible to achieve within the confines of the extended expedition, then engines are invaluable for saving time and effort and can be used with skill to take inflatables through the worst cataracts and rapids safely.

Dress

On most hot weather expeditions members wear gym shoes or hockey boots to support the ankles, shorts, vest and headgear to protect themselves from the fierce rays of the sun. Lifejackets and crash helmets are worn as a drill in every cataract or rapids. Non-swimmers should wear lifejackets on the river all the time.

Lifejackets

A closed cell PVC jacket is adequate as it lifts the head clear of the water. If it becomes torn or ripped, little, if any, buoyancy is lost. Unlike the inflatable lifejacket, these buoyancy aids cannot be inflated above the 15 lbs or so of inherent buoyancy. Now very popular amongst canoeists, these 'wild-water' jackets enable the wearer to swim out and under stoppers and reversals while the closed cell foam also helps to keep the wearer warm in cold water.

Life preservers of the full jacket style are by far the best. They give maximum buoyancy and lift the head and shoulders well clear of the turbulent water, allowing the man in the water to see obstacles ahead of him as he is swept down the rapids.

Every craft should carry one extra lifejacket and every person should have practised floating down a minor cataract to gain confidence in the buoyancy of the jacket and to learn how to travel feet first down chutes and through stoppers before the expedition begins.

Crash helmets

Plastic crash helmets can be hung on the side of the tubing when not in use, but when worn for rapids they should be secured by a chin strap and worn well forward on the head to protect the temples from collision with rocks in the water. Helmets should be of the light aerated type worn by most slalom canoeists.

Gloves

Unless you have well calloused hands it is advisable to wear gloves on an extended expedition otherwise blisters and sores may well impede your rowing.

WHITE WATER TECHNIQUES WITH INFLATABLES

Just as no sensible man will take a yacht out into a storm if he has no knowledge of winds, tides, his boat and crew, so should no man take a rubber inflatable through severe rapids and cataracts until he has learned rowing and paddling techniques on milder rivers and is fully confident of his skills.

Traditionally, one rows a boat blind, looking over one's shoulder for obstacles. In white water, the oarsman faces downstream over the bows of his craft, but rows the boat backwards with short strokes to slow down the craft to give him more time to manoeuvre.

The crew are split evenly with two men in the forward compartment with paddles helping to pivot the craft on the instruction of the oarsman or to ward off oncoming boulders or rocks as well as checking for underwater obstacles. Two men are at the rear of the craft, if there is space between the tubes, and all the expedition equipment secured immediately behind the oarsman on the rowing frame.

THE FERRY GLIDE

The strength of an oarsman is puny against the power of the river. He can do little except turn the craft into the best angled position to allow the force of the current to drive the craft past obstacles. The most common and effective technique to do this is called the 'ferry glide'.

In order to get round the obstacles in the diagram, a touch of the left oar will turn the bows 45° to the current so that the

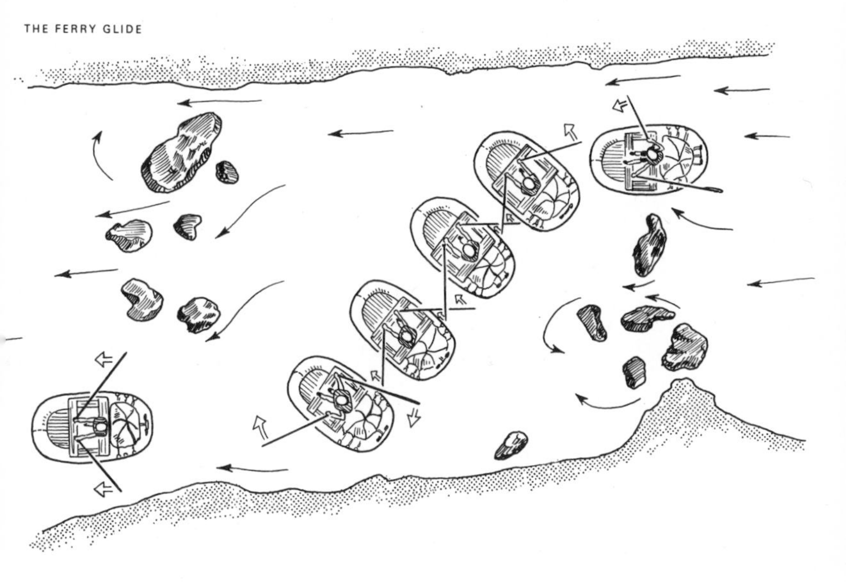

THE FERRY GLIDE

oarsman is now facing the bank from which the obstacle protrudes. If he continues to back row and face the bows at the obstacle maintaining his 45° angle, the power of the water hitting the left side of the craft will glide the craft across from one bank to another and thus safely past the obstacle.

Back rowing in white water requires practice because the oarsman must lift his blades well clear of the turbulence and make solid, powerful short strokes, much different from the smooth, long, deep strokes on calm water. If the blades remain in the water too long they can be jerked from the oarsman's grasp forcing him to lose control of the craft.

PORTAGEE

In moderate water only, it is possible to push the oars and force the bows in the direction required. This is not a powerful stroke because the legs are not being used as in normal rowing, only the arms and trunk muscles.

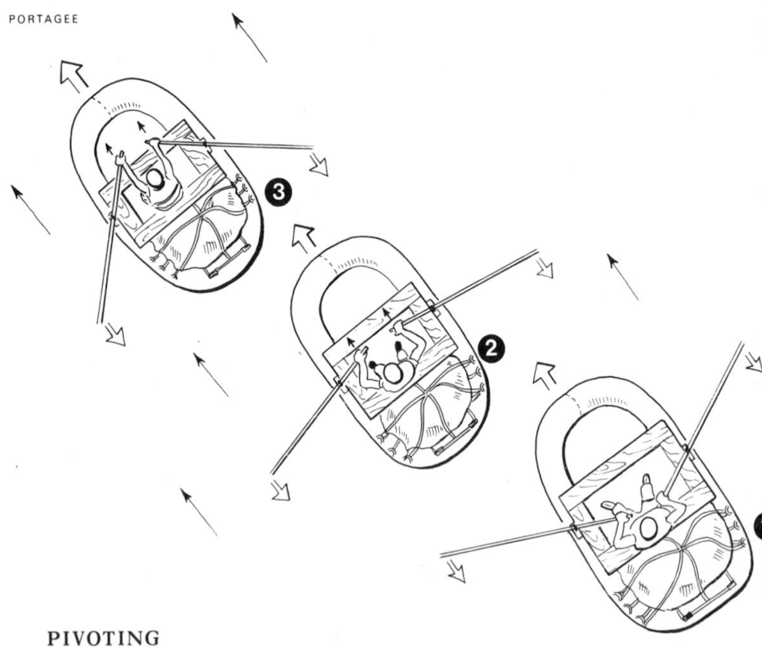

PIVOTING

Unlike a craft powered only by paddles, the oarsman is in a position to pivot the craft in its tracks by taking alternating strokes—one oar powered through the water in one direction, the other returning through the air, then vice versa.

On boulder-strewn stretches of the river it is often necessary to pivot the craft suddenly in order to face up to a narrow gap between rocks. Once the point of entry is positioned, often using great exertion and power from the legs to do it, the oars are held alongside the craft as it squeezes between the rocks. If he fails to ship his oars quickly they can be smashed on the rocks doing damage to the craft and knocking it out of control. If he fails to pivot and make the correct entry between the rocks he could hit the rock broadside and wrap his inflatable against the rock projecting the crews into the water (see *Emergencies* pp. 195–6).

LINING

Not every stretch of river is runnable. In cataracts, where confinement creates great speed and turbulence often forming chutes of water, it is frequently impossible to by-pass such obstacles. For the sake of safety and to save damaging the boat, this is the time to line through the chute with ropes from the bank.

The bow and stern lines attached to every craft are used for this manoeuvre. After it is beached above the chute, one member of the crew walks below the waterfall with the end of the bowline, making sure that the line runs unsnagged through the

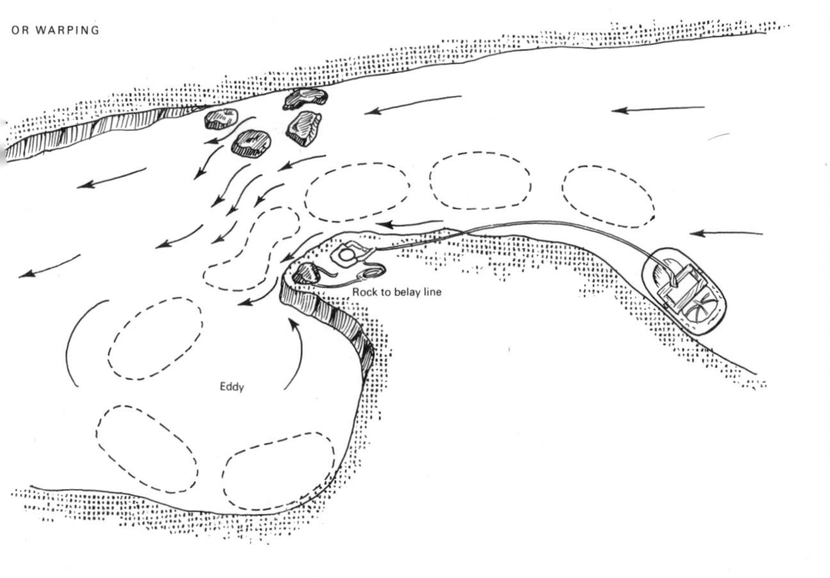

water. Another member of the crew holds on to the stern line playing it out carefully. On a signal, the stern man eases his grip on the stern painter and allows the power of the water to take the craft down the chute. Once over the obstacle the boat can be pulled into the bank with the ropes. If there are sharp rocks or other obstacles within the chute it is advisable to portage the craft along the bank rather than risk ripping the tubes or the hull.

RUNNING WHITE WATER RAPIDS

After the foot reconnaissance of any rapid there is a drill before attempting to run it. The skipper returns and briefs his crew and checks the order in which the boats within the flotilla are to proceed. He checks every crew member's lifejacket, ensures that crash helmets and gym shoes are worn, secures all the equipment and makes sure that all small items such as sun glasses, books and loose gear are packed safely away in sealed containers. Finally he checks that there are no loose lines or painters which could become entangled in people's feet once in the rapids.

Usually one boat within the flotilla will tackle the rapid at a time. It will then wait at the bottom of the rapid in an eddy pool or calm water whilst the second and then third crew attempt it. They are available as a safety craft in case the second or third craft should capsize and life-saving lines can be ready for instant use.

Once his crew are ready to run the rapid the oarsman must manoeuvre his inflatable with a ferry glide or portagee into a good position for entering the tongue of the rapid. He must ensure the bows are pointing downstream as the craft slips over the lip of the rapid. Now, as the craft picks up speed and the roar of the waves deafens any shouting, adrenalin is released and the excitement begins. As the craft rides up the first haystack or standing wave the oarsman must take the opportunity to look

13. Avon *Professional* in the Nzilo rapids during the Zaïre River Expedition of 1974–5.

well ahead for further hazards and evaluate whether or not his original planned route is feasible. If not, he has to think and act quickly. He will have to shout loud over the roar of the water to give instructions to his paddlers as he manoeuvres his craft past obstacles, holes or reversals. As the power of the water begins to take hold of his craft and the waves crash against the tubing in a flurry of foam he will often have great difficulty in recognizing the current route. If things go wrong he may cannon into rocks and spin the boat out of control. When he makes it through to the smooth water beyond, where the safety craft is waiting, the sense of elation is tremendous. But if, by chance, whilst in the rapid, a rock looms up and he is unable to fight hard enough on the oars to spin the craft around the obstacle, he may be forced into the first emergency action.

EMERGENCIES

COLLIDING WITH A BOULDER

The thick skin of an Avon inflatable can take enormous punishment and will often bounce the craft off the rock into the

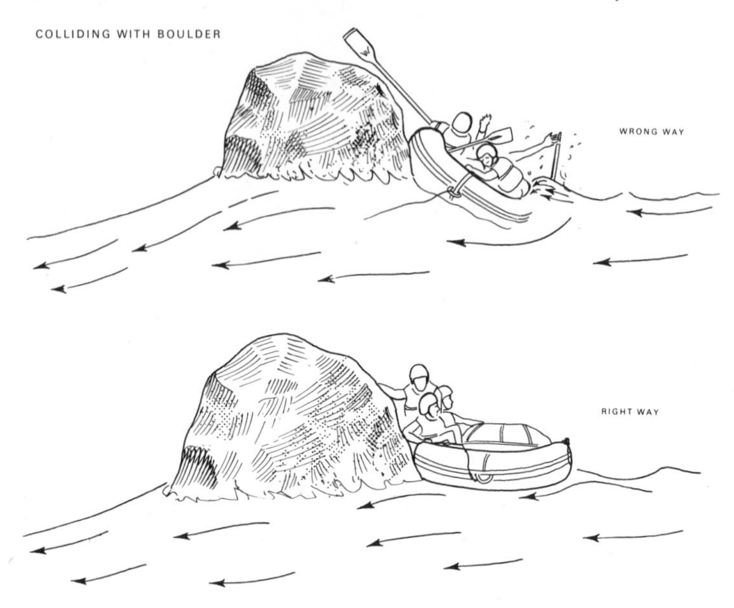

raging current but if the boat hits a large boulder with its broad side then . . .

Emergency 1

The entire crew should immediately jump to the side of the craft nearest the rock.

If the crew do not respond fast enough to the oarsman's warning cry, the side hitting the rock will ride up the boulder and water will pour over the upstream tube sucking it down until the whole craft is wrapped against the rock under great pressure.

FREEING A WRAPPED CRAFT

If the boat should wrap, there is the possibility that the crew may be able to clamber on to the boulder on which the craft is pinned. By concerted effort, pulling and heaving, it is sometimes possible for the crew to ease the boat to one side. Once the craft is freed from the pressure, the crew should leap into the water holding on to the lifelines and follow the craft as it bounces its way through the rapids. If the craft is symmetrically balanced on the boulder there is little chance of moving it. Assistance is required in this case from the crew of one of the other craft who will have to clamber on to the bank closest to the boulder with long lengths of rope or line. This manoeuvre is far from simple and may take anything up to an hour before the lines are secured and the crews

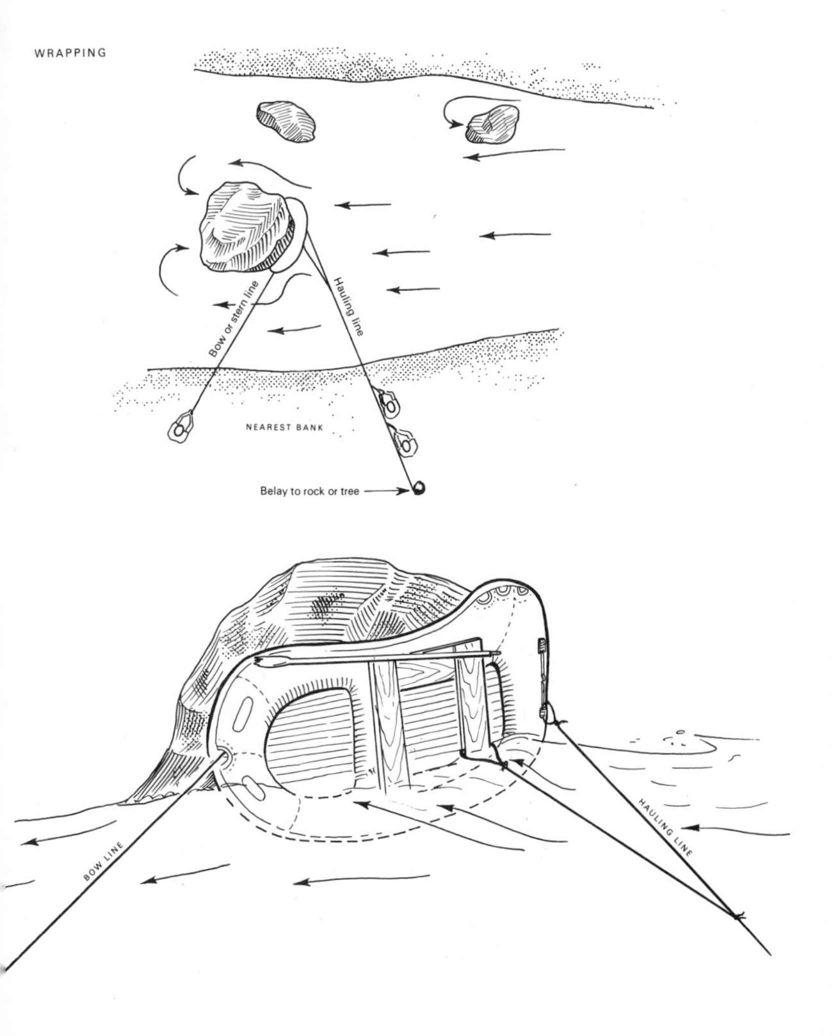

in position to haul the boat off the rock. Loops or knots on the hauling line will assist the crew to heave the pinned craft free.

CAPSIZE DRILLS

When a craft gets out of control and is sucked towards a stopper wave, the crew should crouch as low as possible and hold on to the inner lifeline like grim death. Sometimes the weight of the crew and the lower centre of gravity will allow the up-reared craft to fall back in an upright position. However, if it should flip or capsize, the crew members will find themselves jettisoned into the water. It is a comfort to know that when they come to the surface, the upturned boat will be close at hand.

Emergency 2

After capsizing make to and hold on to the craft.

A crew that manages to stay with their boat and not be spread out all along the river will be comparatively safe as long as they remember to hold on to the upstream side of the craft and manoeuvre themselves so that they are not crushed or cannoned into rocks. If possible, they should reach for the straps on the overturned hull and pull themselves free of the water. Once in comparative safety, look for the other members of the crew and check them off in case someone is trapped underneath. Stay with the craft until it reaches calm water and then pick up the floating paddles which are attached by line, clamber on to the upturned bottom and paddle the inflatable to the bank, where it can be shipped and turned upright with ease. All craft should carry an emergency beaching line on its stern. This line is coiled in between bungies like parachute rigging and can only be released by unclipping the flap and pulling the brightly coloured end of the line, thus releasing it from the elastic bungies. If paddle power is insufficient to ground the craft then one member of the crew can swim to the bank with the emergency beaching line in order to assist with this beaching manoeuvre.

It is almost impossible to right an overturned boat in water because of the weight of the equipment on the rowing frame. A well-practised and strong crew with teamwork can right the craft by pulling on the straps along the bottom, but it is far quicker to paddle or pull the boat to the bank.

Once the craft is on the bank, check every member of the crew and attend to any first aid that is necessary. Then check for punctures or rips and inspect the equipment for loss or damage. Once everything is accounted for allow your crew to have a rest and calm down after the excitement before continuing on your way.

MAN OVERBOARD

In really rough water a member of the crew can sometimes be swept overboard without anyone else realizing. If he is wearing the recommended lifejacket it is not quite as bad as it first seems. But the man overboard must not forget that the oarsman's first responsibility is to his craft and the crew still in it, so he will not want the man in the water to hinder his manoeuvres, nor will he be in a position to help him until they are both through the rapids and in calmer water. So once a man is overboard he is on his own.

Emergency 3
Keep calm, shout and wave to the crew and, once acknowledged, swim downstream with your feet out in front of you.

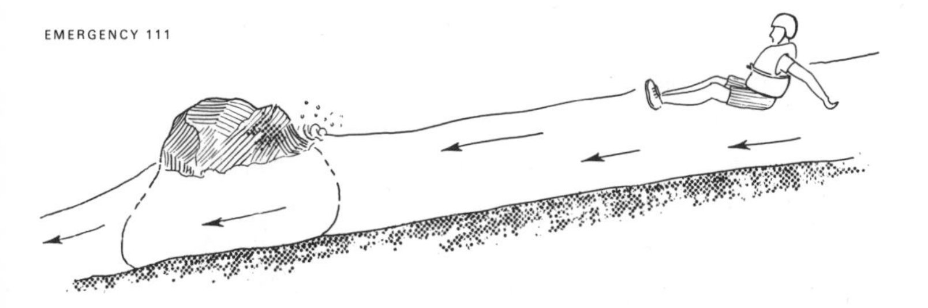

The crew will have been instructed by the skipper to hold fast on the inside lifeline in white water and not to go to the aid of someone who has been swept overboard, unless that person foolishly has not got his lifejacket on securely and therefore requires immediate help. The man overboard will be pulled from the water by his friends once they have reached smooth water. Whilst travelling through the rapids the man overboard must use his common sense, taking gulps of air whenever he can. He should not fight the current unless trapped, otherwise he will quickly exhaust himself.

PARTIALLY SUBMERGED TREES

Avoid being swept into such obstacles at all costs as you may well be trapped in the branches and drowned.

CANOES AND KAYAKS

All inflatables—even the smallest—are cumbersome and, if manually propelled, move slower than the speed of the water in order to retain steerage. Canoes and kayaks, on the other hand, can move faster than the water through which they are travelling. As rapid river boat movements and navigational problems remain the same for both kayaks and inflatables, perhaps a few paragraphs on canoe techniques—based on material supplied by Chris Hawkesworth—would be valuable to the prospective expedition organizer. More often than not extended kayak expeditions use raft support to enable them to travel any distance from a base camp.

In the British Isles the word 'canoe' covers all types of canoe and kayak, whereas in fact a canoe is based on the traditional Canadian design. Decked in, the paddlers kneel and use a single-bladed paddle. Whereas the kayak is based on, and evolved from, the Eskimo kayak where the paddler sits and uses a single double-ended paddle.

Nowadays the majority of 'wild water' canoes are manufactured from fibreglass resin. One British Army unit on an expedition in Kenya could not find enough room in the transport plane for their twelve canoes so, rather than leave some of their stores behind, a fibreglass mould, together with enough raw materials for the canoes, was taken instead. When the party arrived in Africa they made camp in the bush and set about moulding their canoes under the nearest tree. In the warm climate the polyester resin set quickly and easily and inside a week they had their twelve canoes complete and ready to start a five-week expedition. After the expedition the canoes were donated to some of the local population.

Apart from the obligatory crash helmet and lifejacket, personal kit will vary with each individual and the temperature of the water anticipated during the expedition. Even in warm countries the rivers can be very cold, particularly if glacier fed. In this case a wetsuit of the skin diver's type, either a complete suit or a variation of separates, is essential. Many paddlers find the arms of a wetsuit are a problem when paddling over long distances, as the persistent stretching of the neoprene results in prematurely tired arm muscles. The paddler needs to balance the possibility of prolonged immersion in water with his comfort while paddling. In warmer waters a light nylon shirt under a paddling anorak or 'cag' which in turn is worn under a lifejacket is quite adequate. The 'cag' is manufactured out of a waterproof nylon with a mandarin type collar, neoprene cuffs and an elasticized waist. Since the water will come over the paddler's head on larger rapids a 'cag' is regarded as essential.

The probable necessity for quite a long swim with the attendant problem of collision with rocks means that a pair of close-fitting jeans is preferable to a swimming costume because of the protection afforded to the legs from abrasion on the rocks. In a tropical river jeans also help to avoid irritant sores.

The slalom kayak

The high volume slalom-type kayak, 4 metres (12′ 3″) long × 60 cm (24″) wide and 30 cm (12″) deep and weighing 30–35 lbs, has proved to be the most popular for river running. In this section we only consider the wild water kayak. Although smaller than a canoe, it is much more stable and easier to right after a capsize, using the Eskimo roll technique. Here we are more involved in expeditioning with kayaks than with how to paddle a kayak forwards or backwards. It is therefore assumed that anyone going on or planning an expedition will already have a thorough knowledge of all the kayak strokes. The Eskimo roll is an essential technique to be mastered by anyone involved on a kayak expedition. Canoeing on a difficult river can be likened in danger and excitement to climbing a steep rock face or high mountain. If a climber falls he is safe in the knowledge and belief that his rope will save him—but if his rope fails to take the strain he cannot fly. Similarly a canoeist, although he has no rope, can always swim, though swimming in the wrong direction can have the same dire results as for the unfortunate ropeless climber.

A canoeist upside down in a rapid would find it considerably easier, less dangerous and less troublesome to roll than it would be to bale out. The most generally accepted method is the 'screw roll' where the canoeist does not have to move his hands from the paddling position. (Some Eskimo rolls involve the holding of the 'blade' end with one hand.) As all wood shafted kayak paddles are ovalled, the experienced paddler is able to sense where the paddle is in relation to his body and is therefore much more capable of controlling his descent once he has righted himself. It would be an advantage to practise the vertical paddle variant of a screw roll; in a rapid or stopper, the normal surface stroke of the roll is unlikely to work as the white crests of the waves are more air than water. It therefore becomes necessary to lower the stroke and allow the blade to cut through the green water. To give this stroke still more strength you conclude the movement by slightly twisting the blade and pulling over your shoulder as if throwing a shovelful of sand behind you. While sounding complex, these rolls would be executed by an experienced paddler in a matter of seconds.

The major disadvantage of the wild water kayak is the lack of equipment space available due to the area demanded not only by the canoeist's legs but also the substantial blocks of polystyrene necessary for buoyancy. The bulk of the equipment has to be stored in the stern, consequently making a considerable difference to the handling and performance of the canoe.

It has therefore been found necessary to support kayaks during their journeys, either by frequent re-supply from the bank every two or three days, or by having immediate raft support. This is where the inflatables actually run the river, with the kayak being used as a reconnaissance vessel; a couple of kayaks running the rapids before the inflatables can radio back to the main group invaluable first hand information about what to expect.

In conclusion it could be said that a kayak has little or no use with a scientific expedition, but for the sheer excitement and enjoyment of river expeditions it has few rivals.

9. CAVING

by Russell Gurnee

Caves conjure up thoughts of dark, mysterious and forbidding places—each person imagining them differently. Today's man might see a cave as a dangerous and unknown burrow. Yesterday's man, our primitive ancestor who was threatened by predatory beasts and harsh climate, might have seen a cave as a sanctuary providing protection and security.

Hundreds of generations of men occupied some of the entrances of caves in France, Spain and elsewhere in Europe. Some of these men took torches in hand, sought out remote chambers, and left marks and drawings which recorded their visit. We have no way of knowing whether these were the first caving expeditions or whether they were but solitary searchings by individuals who performed magic by drawing an image of an animal in order to improve chances for success on a hunting trip.

During the Ice Age in Europe, the weather forced some mammals south to the Pyrenees and Alps. Chilling blasts from the advancing ice made the shelter of caves relatively comfortable. Man, with his knowledge of fire, survived; but some larger mammals were not able to adapt. One such beast, now extinct, was the European cave bear, *Ursus spelaeus*, one of the largest carnivores in the world. He weighed nearly a ton and stood 2 metres to the shoulder. This fearsome animal retreated underground and was a competitor with man for the sanctuary offered there. Compared with the enormous cave bear, man was an insignificant creature. However, he had the advantage of weapons consisting of stone axes and flint knives, as well as fire and the superior cunning which allowed a contest between these desperate antagonists. Man discovered that during winter when the land was covered with snow and the temperature turned water to stone, the bears retreated to the remote portions of some caves to hibernate. Evidence shows that these primitive men mustered up courage, sought out some of these bear dens and killed the animals as they slept. In certain caves in southern France, the rounded pits of clay can still be seen and in them the partial skeletons of the bears who had been slaughtered—their skulls crushed and limbs severed by primitive tools.

Excursions such as these might have been the earliest expeditions into caves. They had all of the necessary prerequisites for an expedition: preparation, determination, courage, organization, goal and chance of success. These requirements are still as pertinent today, whether the expeditionaries attempt to go to the moon, follow an unknown river or seek an answer to the behaviour of a little-known jungle animal.

Cave exploration presents problems which are unlike most expeditions, for the goal is sometimes undetermined. The explorer is continually faced with the unknown at each turn. There is no certain way he can predict a route; he must explore it. The mountain climber has the advantage of a clearly defined goal, namely the summit. It is true that he may not be able to achieve the summit by the route he has first chosen, but the summit is there for him to attain; the destination is clear. He can prepare his attack with the knowledge of obstacles quite clearly seen. The major part of his energies can be expended in reaching the top as gravity and mechanical techniques will help his return.

The cave explorer must estimate half of his strength, for it is as difficult to return as it is to enter and in fact sometimes is more so should the entrance be made by means of a pit. There is no short cut out of a cave; one must retrace one's steps, climbing out of a pit so easily descended, crossing an abyss so readily spanned earlier, and return to the starting point. No wonder the final aim of the fatigued caver sometimes becomes 'enough strength to reach the entrance.'

This perpetual challenge of the unknown seems to be the greatest attraction for the speleologist. If he engages in the underground study of a specific discipline such as biology, zoology or geology, he gets double satisfaction from his search, for he has the special and appealing environment of the cave and the attraction of his scientific curiosity to cause him to persevere and search through the labyrinth.

One of the earliest expeditions has left us a heritage visible in many caves we visit today. This is the legendary excursion of Theseus, the Greek hero who ventured into the Labyrinth on the island of Crete. Theseus planned to slay the Minotaur—half man, half bull—who fed on Athenian youth. The location of the original Labyrinth is uncertain, but it might have been a natural cave where the monster was reported to live. Theseus was aided by Ariadne, daughter of King Minos of Crete, who knew the secret of the route into the Labyrinth. To find his way back, should he be successful in slaying the Minotaur, she gave him a ball of twine to stretch out in the passageway. Theseus did slay the beast and followed the string through the maze to safety. This ancient myth has been the cause for thousands of miles of string to be found in caves all over the world.

While the goals of early man in caves were to find shelter or seek food, the modern goals are far more complex. It is only in the past two hundred years that any scientific study in caves has been made, providing theories as to their formation and their relationship to surrounding terrain. In the 1700s researchers struggled with the problem of explaining the archaeological remains found in caves, attempting to fit them into the time delineations in biblical texts. Bizarre explanations blending facts with myth and folklore appeared in the serious writings of the day.

It was not until the latter part of the next century that we can say that speleology was established by Edouard Martel, a French lawyer who was fascinated by the underground. As a true sportsman of the era of mountain climbing gentlemen, he devoted nearly all of his adult life to seeking out and exploring caves. He sponsored, equipped, led and participated in expeditions that revealed such remarkable French caves as Padirac, an underground river now open to the public, and Aven Armand, with its spectacular and unusual formations. In England he made the first descent into Gaping Ghyll, a fearsome abyss in Yorkshire. This exploit was the landmark in cave exploration in England which encouraged many others to carry out systematic studies of English potholes and caves.

The beginning of the twentieth century heralded an unprecedented interest in caves throughout Europe. Martel was

14. Torches lit the way for the ill-equipped early speleologist as he explored Mammoth Cave, Kentucky.

established as the most visible exponent of the art; and he added to the scope of his studies by travelling to Italy, Germany, Africa, England and Ireland. Each of these countries had its enthusiasts; and many discoveries were made in the first decade of this century. This was the splendid age for individual exploration; it was the time of the race for the poles, the search for rare animals which formed the basis for the first museum collections, and the beginning of the age of flight. These early explorers became lionized as the outstanding men of the hour.

This euphoria was dashed by the holocaust of the First World War, and many of the enthusiastic and energetic young men who would have contributed to great discoveries poured out their lives at Flanders.

After the war speleology, not thoroughly accepted by the scientific community as a serious study, began a revival and some remarkable discoveries were made in the caves of Italy, Middle Europe, France and Spain. Organizations were established in universities and museums which provided a method for the publication of data accumulated. Just when the scientific work of speleologists began to be recognized, Europe was again plunged into war, this time a conflagration which was to draw all of the major powers into conflict—the Second World War. Speleology was pushed aside for the task of survival and later reconstruction.

The United States, even though its mainland had not been threatened by either of these wars, lagged behind Europe in studying caves. It was not until 1940 that any organized effort was made to consolidate any of the information individually gathered into a common repository. In that year, the National Speleological Society was formed by William J. Stephenson, a Washington patent attorney who enjoyed caves for the sport. During the early years of the Society he interested and encouraged both sport cavers and serious scientists in supporting the organization. Today this is the largest single membership organization devoted to caves in any country, providing publications and communications regarding the caves of the United States.

Prior to the formation of the National Speleological Society, there had been a number of expeditions into caves sponsored by universities and museums to study either a specific natural or archaeological feature. The Smithsonian Institution in 1879 made a report on newly discovered Luray Caverns in Virginia. While the report was principally descriptive, some work was done on the biology and mineralogy of the cave. In 1898 the Peabody Museum in Boston sponsored an expedition to the hill caves of Yucatan. Known as the Corwith Expedition, members searched for possible Neolithic remains in the New World hoping to make similar discoveries to those which had been made in European caves. The trip was well documented and the archaeological work was of first order, but the conclusions reached—that Indians did not use caves for religious purposes—delayed further work in this direction for nearly fifty years. In 1924 the National Geographic Society sponsored a trip to Carlsbad Caverns, New Mexico, to explore that huge cave. The results of that expedition encouraged the government to make the area a National Park.

In 1954 the National Speleological Society sponsored its first expedition to study Floyd Collins' Crystal Cave in Kentucky. This was a multi-disciplinary study which combined the abilities of various scientists and speleologists. The leader was Joseph Lawrence, a young engineer who had tasted the excitement of this huge cave system and felt it deserved a more thorough study. A period of one week was allotted to attempt to unravel its mysteries, and more than fifty people participated in the experiment. In retrospect, perhaps it was the ultimate in presumption to devote only one week to what has become the longest cave in the world, with one hundred and sixty miles of mapped passageway. But at the time of the expedition there were about seven miles known and mapped.

The basic plan was to establish a base camp within the cave

and to have a relay team supply it from the surface, while the explorers, researchers and mappers spent the week underground extending the cave survey. It quickly became apparent that this was an inefficient way to proceed because of the depleting effects of seven days and nights underground. However, the expedition can be considered a success as it served as a basis for further study and explored one manner which could be employed to accomplish the mapping work.

The cave was too large, too complex to be vanquished by a single massive effort. However, the Floyd Collins' Crystal Cave Expedition was a turning point in American speleology, for it provided a base for organized exploration. A method had been initiated for launching a team effort which focused on the study of a total cave, not just one facet or portion of a system.

A similar method can be applied to any systematic exploration. Simply stated, the requirements for any expedition are:

1. A clear definition of the quest.
2. Some knowledge of the intended goal.
3. The general perimeters of what is to be accomplished.
4. The personnel, resources and equipment to perform the task.

The most important ingredient of the above is the clear definition of the quest. If this can be stated in a few words, it has greater impact on the plans that follow. History shows the great explorations to be simple in quest: Reach the North Pole, find the Northwest Passage, put a man on the moon. These great quests were geographical, but there were other great adventures that were extremely technical and complex which can still be defined simply: Split the atom, find a way for man to fly, explore the bottom of the ocean.

Cave exploration may not have any of the far-reaching implications of the above quests, but it does have definite areas of mystery that can capture the imagination and interest of all. The Floyd Collins' Crystal Cave Expedition provided such a challenge, and a number of the participants of the expedition grasped this quest and continued to build upon the study so that through perseverance they could attain the goal of the longest cave in the world.

Perhaps the first knowledge of the intended goal came from Edouard Martel when he visited the Mammoth Cave area thirty years before and predicted that this was one of the great cave regions of the world.

The original exploratory team in the area were dedicated cavers and scientists, all members of the National Speleological Society. Several of them—Philip Smith and Roger Brucker—founded the Cave Research Foundation in order to continue to expand the knowledge of this particular phenomenon—the Kentucky karst region. The challenge attracted a fine team of enthusiasts, however the accomplishment proved more difficult than any of them could have imagined. Many thousands of man-hours were to be spent underground by hundreds of researchers before they succeeded. In fact, twenty years were to elapse before a team of eight speleologists were to make the connection between Floyd Collins' and Mammoth Cave. This connection joined two great cave systems and made it possible to travel beneath the Kentucky woodlands for more than 256 kilometres without surfacing.

The work on this system refined and developed the science of cave expeditions in the United States and provided a base for future expeditions wherever they might be throughout the world.

Fundamentally, cave exploration is an individual study. It is not practical to provide a mass approach. There are mechanical aids which can be provided, but they usually are individual aids and extend the reach of only one person in his traverse through a cave. Each man must crawl, climb, wade and slither through the maze by himself, his companions able to provide only the back-up necessary in case of emergency. There is also the limitation of the route through a cave. The way to return is the way initially gone; there is rarely an alternative. Each caver must exert caution not only for himself but for the benefit of the entire party, as any injury which disables an individual can also cripple the entire team.

With the assumption that caving is an individualistic endeavour, how does one prepare an expedition which is to be a team effort? The Cave Research Foundation approached the problem by discarding the 'camp within the cave' method used on the initial expedition and substituted the assault method, by which platoons of competent individuals in top form entered the cave to the limit of their endurance and returned to base to map their findings. This change in organization came about slowly by trial and error and finally resulted in the technique which was to

15. A team surveying stream passages in Agnes Buenas Cave, Puerto Rico.

be used to make the successful traverse which joined the two major cave systems.

The basic hook on which the method depended was extensive and accurate mapping. The maps were located at a control centre located on the surface where an accurate record was also kept of where each explorer was in the cave at any given time. This knowledge eliminated the need for telephones or radio contact. Each team was self-dependent and operated freely during the course of a limited time schedule. If the team exceeded the time allotted, back-up teams were dispatched to aid them. It is evident that this system will work only when individuals are expert, disciplined and well briefed. Leadership at the platoon level is mandatory. Each team that discovered new territory would carefully map that region and this would be added to the master map at headquarters. This systematic and laborious plotting of the cave has resulted in the most complete and thorough cartographic coverage of any major cave in the world.

The karst region of Kentucky is particularly remarkable because of its producing caves which have passages which extend horizontally for enormous distances, crawlways of seeming interminable length and numerous entrances to the surface—all in a temperate climate with relatively dry conditions. Unfortunately these conditions are quite rare in the world. Expeditions to other caves might require other methods, for the climatic conditions might be near freezing or there may be water-filled passages, huge pits or sudden flooding.

In Canada, for example, a group under the leadership of Dr Derek Ford has explored a cave called Castleguard in Banff National Park, Alberta. This group, the Cave and Karst Group of Canada, has mapped more than 11 kilometres of Castleguard, which extends beneath the Columbia Ice Field—the largest ice mass remaining in the Rocky Mountains. This is a fossil cave, derived from the water that formed it in the melting of the glacier and ice above. For the past 8,000 years, Ford estimates, the cave has been dry, and only the first 800 metres of the discharge entrance floods during spring freshets. This presents enough risk however to affect the exploration of the cave and limits its study to the winter months when the surface above is frozen. In spite of the hazards, several expeditions have reached a point beneath the Ice Field where the passage terminates in a solid ice plug. Survey shows this to be beneath 370 metres of solid ice.

The logistics of such an exploration require the transport of food, fuel and equipment which would challenge even the most intrepid Arctic explorer. One of the forays employed the services of a helicopter to air drop equipment near the cave entrance while the main party arrived overland on skis. As always the individual expertise of team members is the important basis for the success of an expedition.

On the opposite side of the world in Switzerland, an Alpine cave has been the site of extensive exploration. This cave called Hölloch (Hell Hole) is considered the second longest cave in the world. For many years there was a friendly competition between the speleologists of Kentucky and Switzerland for the greatest number of miles mapped in their respective caves. Until the connection of Floyd Collins' to Mammoth Cave, there was a near dead heat, for there were approximately seventy miles of passage mapped in each cave. With the addition of Mammoth Cave to the Floyd Collins system, there was no further contest, but this in no way diminishes the remarkable exploration made by the Swiss explorers, as the two caves are alike only in their immense size.

Each is distinctive in pattern and problems. Mammoth/Floyd Collins is relatively warm, dry and level. Hölloch is cold, wet and steeply pitched, an underground conduit for the melt water from the frozen glaciers of the Alps. Access to this cave is through a small natural tunnel that whistles and screams owing to the wind that pours out of the huge chambers within. The temperature is near freezing and the chill factor of the air numbs the speleologist.

Hölloch was first entered in 1902, but it was not until a young school teacher, Alfred Böegli, took a number of Boy Scouts there in 1952 that any serious study was made. The first trip was a near disaster, as the party was trapped by rising water and spent ten days underground at near freezing temperatures before they could escape. In spite of this inauspicious beginning, Böegli persevered and over the next twenty years led parties which explored and mapped over seventy miles of passageway. The techniques used in Mammoth could not be employed in Hölloch, as Hölloch had only one entrance and it was mandatory that a camp be set up within the cave to permit searching parties to work from it. Another limitation was that, like Castleguard, it was safe to enter at only certain times of the year when the ice was frozen and the cave entrance relatively dry.

During the twenty years of exploration of these two cave systems, located on different continents and explored by different individuals, there was a growing interchange of information by means of publications regarding the techniques of cave exploration. Scientific knowledge increased; studies were made of the geological structures of the areas; theories of cave origin were postulated; and significant advances were made in the mineralogy of cave formations and dating of archaeological remains. In addition to the scientific advances, there were technical advances which allowed man to explore previously unattainable caves.

Perhaps the most significant advance was the improvement in rope techniques and the ability to descend great distances by means of mechanical devices. For the first fifty years of this century the principal methods of descending pits were ladders (rope and then wire) and winches. These methods have been greatly replaced by improvement in rope manufacture, as woven ropes are available which will not unwind when weight is placed on them at the bottom of a long length.

This heralded the use of rappeling devices (mechanical means of applying friction to a rope to control descent) and more importantly the use of ascending devices. With this development

16. A speleologist prepares to descend a cave pit using a rappeling rack.

of the 'monkey on a string' effect, an explorer can climb a single rope without any external aid.

Soon cavers all over America were developing gadgets to slide down and climb up single ropes. Techniques have now become quite standardized and the safe and practical methods which have resulted have been responsible for some astounding explorations in deep cave pits.

One of the groups in the United States that pioneered the use of these devices in caves was the Texas Speleological Society, a chapter of the National Speleological Society. This group of young, active and energetic speleologists mastered rope climbing techniques and took them to Mexico where they descended a huge pit called Golondrinas, a 400 metre free fall. This was the ultimate in individualistic cave exploration, as the ascent from the bottom of the pit required the physical stamina of nearly an hour of repeated deep knee bends to accomplish the climb up the single rope. Further work in Mexico has plumbed deeper pits and led to further exploration using the single rope technique.

Another technical improvement came from the French who pioneered underwater diving apparatus. This self-contained equipment was designed for open water diving but was soon adapted to penetrate water-filled cave passages. Many famous springs and caverns of Europe yielded their secrets by the use of underwater gear; however this kind of exploration has proved extremely dangerous. A number of fatalities have occurred in cave diving, making it one of the most hazardous of all methods of cave exploration.

Until this free diving technique was developed, it was not possible to explore the caves that exist beneath the sea in various parts of the world. In recent years expeditions in the Bahamas have revealed that undersea caves there can be explored for nearly a mile. George Benjamin of Canada has pioneered the work in the Blue Holes of Andros Island, a location for remarkable undersea caves which are the fossil remains of chambers that were once dry before the submergence of the limestone. Benjamin and his party have found stalactites and stalagmites in tunnels of caves as deep as 65 metres beneath the ocean. An exploration of this magnitude requires an expedition equipped with boats, scuba equipment, powerful lighting and extremely favourable weather conditions.

Intermittent flooding in otherwise dry caves can also present logistical problems for an expedition. At Rio Camuy cave in northwest Puerto Rico, several expeditions which I led attempted to make a traverse along the course of an underground river, the Rio Camuy. The rooms of the cave extend 30 to 65 metres above the level of the river which would seem to eliminate the problem of flooding to the ceiling. However, high-water marks show that the water rises as much as 12.5 metres in constricted areas. I have been in the cave when flooding occurred and the stream which averages 8 metres wide rose in a tidal wave 1 metre high as the water surged down the restricted channel. For this kind of exploration lifejackets are mandatory and rubber boats very advisable.

In spite of technical improvements, there is still the inherent risk to be taken by the explorer on any expedition that attempts to penetrate an unknown area. There are some precautions which can be taken which are completely under the control of the members of the expedition. It hardly needs to be said that the participants should be in the best possible physical condition. It follows that health and sanitary conditions in the field are essential if top form and morale are to be maintained throughout the field work. There are enough hazards of possible infection, bad water and injury without adding to the list such things as bacterial poisoning from some local foods and trench foot. One of the most difficult and necessary activities to maintain on a prolonged expedition is proper preparation of food for all. This requires accurate advance planning, supervision and constant attention. It is not possible or even practical to import a complete meal supply, but it is possible to take precautions which will provide satisfactory meals which will not endanger the exploratory team.

My first experience with the possibility of such a disaster came about on the ship on which I served during the Second World War. There were 1,200 men aboard the repair ship, U.S.S. Ajax, which was anchored in the harbour of Eniwetok in the South Pacific. One morning seven hundred men came down with amoebic dysentery, a tragedy which to them was only slightly less traumatic than the dropping of the atomic bomb. In the ensuing hectic days two men died and the ship was put in quarantine and moved to a remote atoll. It was a week before the cause of the infection was discovered: a plumber in the shipyard where the ship was built had hooked up the salt water line to the potato peeling machine, and contaminated water was being flooded over the food which was served to the men. The ship was out of service for six weeks and those of us who were well enough to serve never forgot the lesson. The chance of food poisoning is often great in underdeveloped back-country areas both because of the methods of growing food and particularly because of the lack of sanitation in preparing it. Encouragement of team members to try all local foods under the reasoning it is all part of the foreign experience can be disruptive to the effectiveness of the expedition.

It has been said by a number of famous explorers that adventure is the result of poor planning. No serious researcher wants adventure on purpose, as, when in hazardous areas, the expedition's goals can be seriously hampered. The professional who has spent time in remote places grasps whatever conveniences he can, when he can. It is not to anyone's advantage to do something the hard and hazardous way if there is a less spectacular, easier and safer way. There is thrill and excitement enough in being the first person to see a virgin cave room or in returning from a strenuous and difficult exploration.

One of the most memorable experiences I have had in a cave was entering a room deep in the interior of Guatemala and finding the undisturbed remains of a human burial as well as the bare footprints of the Mayan Indian who had placed the body there more than a thousand years before. Nothing had been disturbed; and I experienced a great sense of comradeship with these unknown men who burned incense and placed offerings in this sanctuary. They were removed from me only by time, and here in the cave time had stood still. It seemed that I understood the feelings of those first expeditionaries whose purpose for entering caves was fully as important as the quest determined by today's explorers.

10. MOUNTAINS

by Malcolm Slesser

As a start I recommend leaving for the expedition by aeroplane. Not only does this mean that the most dangerous stage is overcome right at the outset, but international air travel is always accompanied by beautiful air hostesses, slap-up meals and duty-free drinks. Cushioned from life's stresses, martini in hand, one can mull over the forthcoming expedition and, in what usually turns out to be a mental tour de force, remember all those things that didn't get done. Now it is too late, and the next 5,000 or so kilometres can be devoted to replanning the expedition in the light of the logistics at one's disposal.

For instance, I once received, as I stepped on the plane to Iceland, a telegram to tell me that the Danish Ministry for Civil Aviation had refused my expedition landing rights in Greenland. By the time I landed in Reykjavik one hour and forty minutes later, not only had I smiled at the several charming stewardesses, drunk my way through half a bottle of gin and eaten wholesomely, but I had even evolved a plan to deal with the Ministry—one that actually worked, though it took two more bottles in a Reykjavik hotel room to convince the Icelandic air company of my proposals.

Mountaineering is a way of life that is really inconsistent with an expedition plan. At its best, climbing mountains is a delicious free expression and some take it to the length of doing without ropes or companions. An expedition by definition is the involvement in a goal. The nasty word 'team' often crops up, and expedition leaders know only too well the delicate path they must tread if they are to form a real team in order to climb a mountain.

Doug Scott on Everest, the hard way (1975 expedition), remarked that during the days when Leader Bonington had them stocking high camps, a 'shop floor' mentality spread through the ranks. Of course, it vanished the moment, he, Scott, was in the summit thrust.

My own experiences stem from the days when almost every climber in an expedition was only a part-time mountaineer. In short, he worked at something else for a living. The expedition was made possible by carving a chunk of time out of one's working life with its short holidays. Often the word expedition was used simply because it made up the concept, allowed one to print notepaper, badger firms for free goods and win diplomatic support. But in fact everyone concerned thought of it as a holiday. In planning an expedition this understandable human foible must be borne in mind. The more serious the objective, the more cash and support one seeks from others, the more one is morally committed to pushing through the effort, the more one has to forgo present joys for future bank balances and esteem. I know many of my expedition companions have never given a tinker's cuss for sponsors or science. The expedition is to be enjoyed and who can foretell which set of circumstances will stimulate most enjoyment? I learnt this the hard way when organizing and leading the 1958 Scottish East Greenland Expedition to the Staunings Alps. One could not have wished for a finer set of companions. But to suggest to any one of them that the expedition had an obligation to its sponsors was to incur an almost vulgar hilarity. Yet that expedition did achieve many notable ascents, some fine exploration, and even some science.

A big mountain, then, has its price—the price of cohesion, of team work, of sinking personal motives in the common good, of not necessarily being in the summit pair. It is very easy to forget this aspect of an expedition in the excitement of planning it at home. One's vision is of the summit, rather than the drag of building up the logistics for that final push, a push you may only actually view through binoculars several thousand feet below.

Sad to say, people do not always go on mountaineering expeditions because of the call of the hills. Some people are just plain ambitious. This problem might never have arisen had not mountaineering become respectable. I recall with pleasure, when, as a student in the early forties, my fellow students thought me crazy to be a climber and the Director of Physical Education nodded sadly when I explained that there was no way we could introduce a Blue for climbing.

All this points to the fact that there is no way one could possibly advise anyone on a mountaineering expedition. There is something, somewhere for every taste. The ambitious can organize the massive onslaughts upon the great peaks and then go out and lead the expedition. That takes some doing and Hunts and Boningtons are thin on the ground. Some expeditions are disastrous. One recalls a certain German veteran who seems constantly involved in lawsuits. The modest, wealthy, or retiring can take off to some remote spot and do their 'thing' quietly and with inner joy. I suppose the driving force for an expedition is really exploration—albeit in a vertical plane. But again this generalization is quite dangerous. To some, vertical spires of unsullied granite ten miles from the road-head represent exploration of the ultimate kind—as in the aiguilles of Patagonia. To others, rounded ice-caps in the remote Arctic give a greater joy. One friend recalled how much he had enjoyed the second ascent of a slag heap in northern Greenland. When I enquired who had made the first ascent, he replied that 'to judge by the turd on the summit it had been a musk-ox'.

But let us put some order in this narrative. The expedition will start with an inner stirring in your being. What or who starts it you may never know. It may be a chance remark in climbers' company or something picked up in a magazine or perhaps the response to some nagging stress in everyday life, until deep down something inside decides to make a break. The decision will have been made long before you recognize it, and certainly long before you have managed to put it over to your wife or your boss or confided it to your friends. It is a delicious moment, just knowing that it has begun. The rest, the organization, the travelling, the actual climbing of the mountain follow as inevitably as day follows night. The mind can take over, the will has done its bit.

We shall exclude from this survey those strange folk who prefer solo expeditions. They need no advice from anyone. But your first task is to find companions who are inclined to your own view. It is a tricky phase of the expedition's planning, because it is always tempting to compromise—the compromise of the objective in order to tempt the right companion or vice versa. Among my own expedition friends there are those I know who regard the mountain as THE thing. For my part I think the companions are perhaps the most important ingredient.

And where to go. The world, which has become so small, has also become damnably expensive. Three years ago one could take charter flights to the ends of the earth. Four hundred pounds would see you to Patagonia, two hundred and fifty to the Peruvian Andes, less than one hundred and fifty to the Yukon and Alaska and about the same to the nearer Himalaya. Greenland was just a stone's throw away and the cheapest of all. Of course I am talking about air fares. The people who really score are the people with time; real time. Not the six weeks vacation or extended leave, but with six months or more. These are the people to envy. The people for whom Stevenson's words apply: 'It is better to travel hopefully than to arrive.'

To these lucky few we also offer no advice, for they have their own timeless paths. One recalls with affection the Marris brothers who were to be found stravaiging across the tundras of northern Greenland, having apparently arrived there upon some broom stick, and travelling so light that one wondered from where they drew their sustenance. Urbane and friendly, they would arrive at one's camp, visit, and leave with the nonchalance of someone who had called for a sherry before dinner.

But most of us have to work, and mountains and mountain expeditions represent some clear cut separation between two ways of life. We may not be the poorer for that, for the change heightens our appreciation, but it also gives us less time to slip into the timelessness that is essential for true enjoyment of an expedition. The pressure of monsoons, the expiry of one's ticket, the closing in of the ice, can all serve to rob us of our best moments. For the mountaineer, it is time, not money, that is the scarce and valued resource.

Air fares have more than doubled in recent years. Small groups can still drive to the Taurus in Turkey or the Hindu Kush, finagle their way to east Greenland, or get to the wilderness areas of Wyoming, Montana and the Canadian Rockies and still get some change out of £200, but the Andes, the Himalayas, northern Greenland, Baffin Island, Alaska, Yukon are much more expensive now, while the southern tip of Patagonia is beyond reach of any but the wealthy or subsidized.

In Europe we are lucky that people, even though they may consider climbers to be eccentrics, are still willing to pay to hear their stories, and so the diligent expedition planner can embark on large budgets in the hope of recouping outlays by winter evening slide-shows and lectures. There was a time when I could go almost anywhere knowing that I could pay off my expenses on my return in this way, but it takes a lot of one's free time and energy. There comes a time when one must decide whether or not to be the full time mountaineer. I recall Whillan's grievous face as he told me how he was still being pursued for expenses of a past trip while he was already planning the next.

So most of us now go in for PR. The advertising industry has been going sufficiently long for the techniques and procedures to be well known and reasonably straightforward. You need brass neck, conviction in the merit of your objective and a great deal of persistence. Through these means you may procure a small amount of money and a large amount of free or cheap equipment and food. But manufacturers eventually become hardened to such requests. I once pestered a manufacturer for twenty-four of his delightful vests. After three weeks he wrote me a curt letter saying he had had enough of such begging and he was through. Hurt that he should confuse us with all those tourists who had previously written to him, I wrote again, pointing out what splendid chaps we were. He sent us two dozen vests with a letter saying he admired our persistence.

One of the most important decisions of the expedition is its title. From long experience I can assure prospective expedition organizers that there could be nothing better than to leave the expedition title, and hence its headed notepaper, until the return. Then and then only can one be sure of having promoted a successful expedition. I have already hinted in the opening paragraph how, during those reflective moments on the flight out, when you discover some frightful omission, you may have to select an entirely new objective. Sponsors have a tedious knack of regarding any other objective than the one mentioned in the letterhead as failure. In my own case, the most striking example was the 1969 Watkins Mountains Expedition. Four of us entertained the crazy notion of going to north-east Greenland—Scoresby Sound settlement to be exact—and boating down the forbidding east coast of Greenland on the southerly current to reach the Borg glacier, which debouches from the then highest unclimbed peak in the Arctic, the Borgtinde. We duly arrived at Scoresby Sound and embarked in our 5 metre open boat trailing a rubber dinghy. Forty hours later we were encamped upon an ice floe having failed to find a way through the ice to the south shore of Scoresby Sound. For a while we enjoyed this bizarre situation, until one of us noticed that the mountains of the nearby Volquarts Boon coast were passing by at a truly astonishing speed and that by the time we had burnt our second cigar we would be far out into the Denmark Strait. With some trepidation we re-launched the boat and finally did gain the shore. Two weeks later, having been buffeted by fifty-mile-an-hour gales and squeezed by dense brash ice which had shaved an inch off the prow of our boat, we entered the blissful calm of Romer Fjord. In a marvellous few days we found hot springs, some hitherto unknown Eskimo ruins, made some botanical 'firsts' and ascended sundry untaxing but rewarding mountains. South of us lay densely packed ice. Regretfully we gave up the attempt to reach the original expedition goal and settled for what we had on the spot. Interviewed by the media on our return, we could not but admit we had failed to reach our objective. Yet if we could only have put off naming our objective until we reached home, called it the Romer Fjord Expedition, we could have gone down in history as one of the most successful four man sorties of all time.

That particular expedition reminds me of another element in the organization. The members of these trips usually have to fulfil many roles in addition to being good mountaineers. Some medical expertise is always welcome. On the brilliant Romer Fjord Expedition I was wise enough to cherish my delicate constitution by having along a doctor and a dentist. To be more accurate I had a man who had trained as a doctor. He had since become a teacher of anatomy. When pressed for medical advice he would always say, 'Don't ask me, ask a real doctor'. However, the dentist was a very real practising dentist and one morning when I injudiciously crunched a prune stone and split a molar in two, I sought his immediate help. He looked at me without interest. 'I'm on holiday,' he announced and continued with his breakfast. 'But surely you've brought some dental first aid?' I asked petulantly. He shook his head and continued to admire the view of the massive bergs floating down Scoresby Sound. Finally, after repeated efforts I managed to engage his interest. Placing me on the ground so that the sunlight could illuminate my mouth he cursorily examined me and then drew back. 'Aye, that'll give you a lot of trouble.' He lost all further interest. The only successful expedition medico I have known was a woman. I have not been able to find out if she was regarded as so successful by the other women on the party.

In principle there would seem to be two types of expedition. The massive ones such as the Everest affairs, where every last

17. Sherpas preparing loads at Camp 1 on the 1970 Annapurna South Face Expedition.

detail has to be worked out ahead, with the material boxed and sent out from home, have been dealt with by Kelvin Kent in the opening chapter. For these one needs good credit or a Barclay card. I would refer here to the smaller affairs.

The question facing the small expedition is whether to get all food and equipment here at home, pack it and send it out or buy everything on arrival. The merit of the former is that all the hard graft is done at home and the expedition is the easier for it, but the snag, and it is a huge one, is that very few countries will allow the import of several thousand pounds' worth of expedition food and equipment duty free. It may be possible to persuade the customs to take a money bond against the re-exportation of one's expedition equipment. This can be done, for example in Peru. The first time I did this all went well. We put down a modest

£400, re-exported most of what we had imported, except the food, and got back the cash. The Peruvian sole was hard currency and we lost little more than the use of the money for eight weeks. The next time however, we were forced to put down £1,000 which we borrowed from a friendly business man. It took us a year to recover it, during which time devaluation of the Peruvian currency had reduced the value of the bond to about three quarters. Some expeditions, in addition, have been forced to pay for material which had been used up, broken ice axes, pitons, ropes and the like.

Nowadays my preference is to fly out light, with everything, but everything in my luggage. A skilled mountaineer can travel with up to 35 kg of luggage for the standard allowance of 20 kg. Boots will be on his feet. His ice axe will be his walking stick (though it's hard to pass off pterodactyls), his coat will be an anorak stuffed with pegs and crabs and a specially strengthened polythene bag will ostensibly be carrying his reading material for the flight. Alas, these anti-hijack screens make it all much tougher.

Once you have arrived in the host country, and this even applies to southern Greenland, you can buy almost all your food on the spot. Personally I am not wildly enthusiastic about tramping around foreign cities in climbing gear and so I tend to head straight for the hills. It's also a good plan to stake out a base for mail and messages. Sometimes a few letters ahead of time can winkle out some friendly embassy man, British Council rep., or foreign businessman. Sometimes one can secure the co-operation of the mountaineering organization, though this has its dangers in those countries where mountaineering is very organized. Once, in Iran, armed with letters of introduction in Persian to various relevant persons, I found that I was really carrying with me an open invitation to be overcharged wherever I went.

It will be at this arrival stage in foreign parts that you begin to find out more about your companions. Bosom pals of the small crags may turn out to have thoroughly irritating foibles, like never doing anything on time, or in extreme cases, never doing anything period. The flesh pots of some foreign cities are so agreeable that a mountaineer out to have a holiday may decide that Lima or Montevideo has more to offer than Huandoy or Fitzroy. A wise leader, keen to get to his peak, will have judiciously arranged for a shortage of funds at this point.

Though it may not always be appreciated as such at the time, the best part of the expedition is getting from the road-head or airfield to the base camp. Even the best and fittest of us usually have some little cross to bear, physical or mental, and that journey into base gives one time to settle. It also gives a chance for people to adjust to acceptable behaviour. On the presumption that you will not have chosen companions totally insensitive to their surroundings, the journey to base provides a means whereby the noisy and extrovert learn just how far their habits are acceptable to the rest, and who enjoys and who does not enjoy their company. The quiet find a means of contacting the others. The shared evening meals are a superb opportunity to relax and build a community, while the morning gives a chance to find out how each person responds to that part of the day when everyone has to put aside his own interest in order to get the show on the road. Often one can spend the whole day on one's own; a rare pleasure that will be lost once on the mountain, when the objective of the expedition and the physical and emotional demands of others will keep one continually in a state of involvement.

Most mountaineers use the journey into base to get fit, since most, though not all, will have made no effort to do so earlier. The wise ones therefore eschew horses or boats. They walk, carrying light packs, to break themselves in. Yet having said that, I can also recall some days of incredible bliss using boats and horses. On our Staunings Alps expeditions, there were the boat journeys up a long magnificent fjord in a powered boat or canoe. These journeys were overwhelming sensory experiences, such was the beauty and grandeur of the scene. And once, going to base camp in the Andes, on horseback, I found that I could collect a sizeable flora, for I had the energy to diverge from the route and the speed with which to catch up with the party by nightfall.

And so to the mountain. The perceptive reader may think that, given a leader of experience and competence, the ascent of the mountain is a foregone conclusion. Not so. For the game of chance has hardly begun. Not only may the mountain reveal hitherto hidden difficulties, but the weather is a factor always beyond one's control. In the mind of the armchair mountaineer this is the part of the expedition where the excitement lies; where there is danger and where lives are at risk; where the mouth goes slightly dry and a certain ghoulish anticipation sets in.

Certainly for the climber there is a sort of rebirth as he steps out of his tent on the first morning at base camp and raises his

18. Any icefall is probably the biggest objective danger on a mountain. An icefall lies near the bottom of the mountain and therefore near the bottom of the logistic pyramid. For every two loads carried up to Camp 5 on the Annapurna Expedition fifteen would have to pass through the icefall.

eyes to the mountain. Whether the mountain looks hard or easy may depend on the light. The climber may feel fear or eager anticipation. Occasionally the mountain may actually repel him. Then because he is one of a team, he may be committed to a course of action he does not like.

I suppose for this reason I have always enjoyed better those expeditions which aimed not at one peak but at a mountain area. Nothing can ever compare with the satisfaction and joy we had in the Staunings Alps in 1958 when almost all the peaks were still virgin. We divided to climb in small parties, sometimes of only two, and each party took a peak that appealed to it. For some it was ice routes, for others steep clean rocks; for others the easiest way up a hard peak. I think we collected seventeen virgin peaks that summer and not one of them had climbing routes of less than 1,000 metres of difficult climbing and many were twice as long. Inverarnan, climbed by Lovat and Bennet from a sea level base camp was one of the lowest peaks in the Staunings (2,160 metres) but it gave 2,000 metres of rock climbing.

The finest expression of mountaineering is discovery and for those of us who are not the greatest technical climbers, the discovery has to come from being in unknown territory. For the highly skilled man, something of the same experience can be obtained from discovering a way up a virgin face or by forging an entirely new route. Both sorts of experience bring that delicious joy when, after difficulty, a way through is found.

Indeed, more than any actual successful ascent, I think I enjoyed two major traverses in the Staunings Alps. The first was from the head of Alpefjord, one of the deepest and most magnificent of the east Greenland fjords, through mountain territory to the south east to reach the remote Eskimo hunting station of Syd Kap, 128 kilometres to the south. For two weeks my companion and I were self sufficient in food and remarkably content. A thrust up a particularly vile looking glacier finally revealed a route, which in turn became a highway through the mountains. Of course, we had seen aerial maps of the territory and we had maps of a sort, but we were the first to cover the actual ground and meet the obstacles at first hand.

A few days after this trip one of my companions suffered from a stone falling on his head and opted out of a party that was to attempt the first crossing of the major part of the Staunings, so I joined in his stead. Two of the group had already reconnoitered the col from the north and were now to attempt its traverse from the south west. Our way ran up a very crevassed glacier through quite stunning mountain scenery, an area later to become the scene of many climbing expeditions before the Danes placed difficulties in the way of one of the world's finest climbing grounds. The excitement mounted as we made for what we hoped would be the south side of the col. We were all sufficiently experienced to know that the col we were making for might turn out not to be the right one. New territory can be very deceptive. We reached the col just as sun was setting on a bitterly cold evening, and to our joy found that it was just as we had hoped. Below, the north side dropped with ferocious steepness into black shadows. With a sense of meeting a crux we retired for the night and woke to a sunny dawn. We almost tip-toed to the col and roped up. The first two rope lengths revealed that the blue-green ice of earlier summer had given way to cramponable snow and we were soon romping down the steep slopes, barely even alarmed when one of us slipped and accelerated over a bump. We held him and in less than an hour were 600 metres lower. The col had been crossed and an important way opened up through the Staunings. We named it Col Major. The final 40 kilometres to the airstrip where the others had foregathered, were as nothing. What an ending to two great months!

Yet the curious thing is that it was not until we were much older that we realized what a successful expedition we had had. No one wrote us up, no radio announced our return. It is only in retrospect that its great success stands out.

Discovery on a big face has a slightly different quality. For one thing it is less carefree. Breaking through the obstacle does not

19. Sherpas carrying some of the eight tons of equipment needed to be brought up from Camp 1 on the Annapurna Expedition.

necessarily mean an easy run down the other side, but the thought of climbing higher with a difficult retreat to come. Yet the momentous excitement of discovering a key passage, the extra effort of technique and will that often goes into it remain as vivid memories long after the view from the summit has been forgotten.

Given a good team spirit this sense of pleasure can actually be communicated to others on the expedition. I recall the excitement with which we listened to the story of the two climbers who had finally discovered a route up the 330 metre wall that protected the great east ridge of Yerupaja in the Peruvian Andes. They roped it and marvelling at the ingenuity of Mike Kosterlitz and Des Hadlum, we followed their fixed ropes up the wall to a minute ledge at the foot of the great east ridge.

One of the troubles about high altitude camping is that one is closely tied to one's companion day and night. In the Arctic or in lesser ranges, one may often take a stroll of an evening or sit far from the tent and take one's ease. High up, the tent site may be nothing but a tiny ledge and outside is deep winter all the year round as soon as the sun sets. The long evening may not always be one of unmitigated pleasure. Perhaps your companion passes wind, which is vile, or perhaps you do, which is almost as bad. The risk of this vulgarity is considerable as one rises in height. I am convinced that climbers should return to baby foods at great heights, for certainly their digestions become as frail as those of an infant. I can truly claim to have caused more suffering in this connection than ever I have experienced. The effect of wind is quite devastating in a small space. The extreme case was when with several others, some of them Russians, I was bottled up in a snow cave at 7,000 metres on Pik Kommunisma. The next day was to be summit day, and though feeling distinctly disinclined to eat, I had forced down some food. As we snuggled into our bags for the night, warm for once, because the snow hole insulated us splendidly from the sub-zero temperature outside, the most articulate of the Russians, mindful of English jesters, remarked, 'No spoiling of the air.' My stomach was churning about and soon I could not help the passage of wind. Finally a disgusted and disgruntled Russian rose, took a spade and dug a ventilator. We breathed air, but shivered all night long.

Another irritating trait is the clumsy tent mate. Climbers cook and eat in their tents. The risks of fire are trivial and the payoff is handsome—a warm fug, thawed out boots and dried out gloves and socks. Nothing is worse, having nursed a pan of snow through the stages of melting to boiling water to soup, than to have one's companion move jerkily and cause the whole thing to spill. Women who know their husbands as clumsy and useless about the house would be astonished to see how most of them are transformed in a tent into creatures of slow, deliberate and careful movement.

My own pet hate is the man who sleeps through every emergency. How nice it would be to continue to sleep while someone else tightened the guy ropes. How nice to have a watchful companion with whom to discuss the contingency plans if avalanches start to fall, or lightning strikes. Some people, the fatalistic, or simply unimaginative, sleep through it all. They are not really to be envied. Climbers who live long do so because they are aware—aware of all the dangers.

I believe that young climbers survive largely through luck. Awareness cannot be taught. It really comes through experience. I recall so many brilliant climbers, now dead, who died young, some not even in the mountains. Theirs was a sort of recklessness, based upon inexperience, with its roots in an inability to know when they were in danger. But survive that early stage and one learns awareness.

Of course we all need luck. I am certainly conscious of being lucky to be alive, yet I have not had one tenth of the hazardous climbing that many others have had. Too many people imagine that safety is synonymous with good equipment, lots of pitons and slings. You cannot really buy safety. It is a state of mind, in which every danger is sensed and evaluated. It is a sense which, when awakened, seldom becomes dormant. It is a sense which makes one man wait till the freeze comes, while another crosses a dangerous slope. The slope may not avalanche, but only the experienced and aware know the risk that was being run.

Risk, of course, is another thing. Sometimes the enterprise calls for risk. But I would a hundred times rather embark upon a calculated risk with an aware climber than with one who blithely takes all risks, having failed to evaluate them. The reason being that you are usually roped to your companion. When he falls you may go too. And falling rocks and avalanching snow are no respecters of mountaineering conventions.

APPENDIX: KIT AND EQUIPMENT

by Kelvin Kent

How much and what

The vast majority of items to be included in any particular expedition are common to most other expeditions. It is usually only the climate or physical geography which dictates the degree of specialist equipment required, and prior knowledge of the area, terrain, climate and seasonal conditions will help a lot in the selection of the right articles for particular tasks and situations.

It is impossible here to list everything but from my experience—which covers jungle, river, overland and mountaineering expeditions—the following is a guide intended as a preliminary check list of important items. They are not in any particular order and I am sure that there are omissions, but I hope they will serve as useful starting points.

PERSONAL EQUIPMENT

Sleeping bag
Rucksack or frame pack
Normal clothing for before and after
Lightweight or heavy duty underwear (Damart is best for cold climates)
Tropical hat or head cover
Sweat rag
Swiss penknife
Washing kit
Soap, toothpaste and shaving kit
Jungle boots or climbing boots
Socks
Suitcase (to leave ordinary clothes in)
Specialist climbing equipment or tropical wear
Mirror (metal is best)
Track suit
Gloves

Gaiters
Torch
Balaclava helmet
Overboots
Lighter
Camera
Housewife
Water bottle
Map case
Plastic bags (various sizes)
Space blanket
Water sterilizing tablets
Eating utensils
Compass
Notebook
High altitude cream

ENGINEER STORES

Toggle ropes and rope ladder
Kit boxes
Lifejackets and safety helmets
Block and tackle equipment
Tifor jack
Winch
Anchors
Earth auger
Hammers, sledge and hand
Oilstone slip
Tool kits, vehicle and general
Saws, hand and power
Electrical testing kit
Torque wrench
Banding machine
Rope
Axes, hand and felling
Identification panels
Picks and shovels
Water cans (5 gallons)
Sharpening stone
Tape measure, 50 metre
Bardic lamps
Ice axes
Climbing ironmongery
Climbing rope
Oxygen cylinders
Crampons
Pitons
Snow stakes
Dead men
Ice screws
Marker canes
Marker flags
Snow shoes
Skis
Foam mats
Torches, waterproof
U2 cells
Cable
Lubricating oil
Fire extinguishers
Shackles and clamps
Compasses and whistles
Inflatable craft
Alloy ladders
First aid kits
Entrenching tools
Helmets
Wetsuits

Swimming flippers
Wire
Jumars
Carabiners
Nylon or polyester cord
Assorted screws, nails, nuts and bolts
Glue: Araldite and Bostik
Berkefeld Filter pumps
Millbank bags
Outboard motors
Fibre glass repair kit
Drills, hand and electric
Snow shovel and snow saw
Loudhailer
Scales
Crapnets
Signs
Parachutes
Marker buoys
Balloon markers
Water containers (plastic)
Funnels
Matchets
Blow lamp
Masking tape

OFFICE STORES

Typewriter and spare ribbons
Stationery
Rubber stamps
Reference books
Prayer book/Bible
Maps and charts
Felt tip pens
Magic markers
Scotchtape
Plastic bags
Ball point pens
Account books
Stapler and staples
Air mail envelopes

SURVEY/NAVIGATIONAL/MEASURING EQUIPMENT

Altimeter
Barometer
Sextant
Abney level
Chronometer
Meteorological recording kit
Binoculars
Tapes
Watches, waterproof
Thermometer
Theodolite
Gravimeter

CAMP STORES

Camp beds
Hammocks
Mosquito nets and covers
Tents (with flys if wet)
Washbowls
Towels

Insecticide
Balls of string
Tilley HPP, and hurricane lamps
Spare wicks
Candles
Chemical light devices
Tables, folding
Camp chairs
Masking tape
Plastic sheeting and/or sized sheets and rolls
Tarpaulins
Vacuum flasks, assorted
Hexamine or Meta fuel cookers
Primus stoves
Gas cookers
Pressure cooker
Pot scourers and cleaning equipment
Elastic straps
Canvas and plastic buckets
Penknives
Gifts
Tent repair kits
Sewing kits
Heaters
Lighting kit
KFS sets
Cans of gas
Mugs
Spare laces
Extra gloves
Spare insoles
Hot water bottles
Books
Games, e.g. Scrabble, pocket chess, cards, liar dice
Tobacco and cigarettes
Straps
Kit bags
Alarm clocks
Leather oil
Spare torch bulbs
Foam mats
Lilos
Hand brushes
Can openers
Toilet paper
Tissues
Matches
Lip salve
Boot polish and dubbin or Suppletect
Boot brushes
Cassette tapes (pre-recorded music)
Padlocks
Fishing tackle
Can openers

RATIONS AND COOKING

Composite pre-packed rations
Dehydrated rations
Local purchase rations
Sponsored rations

Survival rations
Liquor
Cleaning liquids, powder and scourers
Cleaning materials
J cloths, paper towels
Matches, can openers
Plastic tubing, assorted
Plastic bags, assorted
Plates and cups (Tupperware or Melaware)
Hand cleaners
Kitchen knives
Billicans
Kettles
Frying pans
Saucepans
Ladles

PHOTOGRAPHIC EQUIPMENT

Cameras
Film; colour and black and white
Cine camera, 8 mm with 300 m lens
Cine camera, 16 mm
Sound equipment for 16 mm cameras
Plastic bags and containers with labels

SCIENTIFIC STORES

British Museum or Scientific Body stores
Dissecting kit
Plastic jars
Zoological scales
Fishing equipment
Nets
Formalin

MEDICAL STORES (See also Chapter 2, pp. 72–3)

First aid packs
Paludrine or anti-malaria tablets
Water testing kit
Water purifying tablets
Antiseptic creams
Plasters
Plastic skin
Insect repellents
(Main medical stores and drugs will obviously be made up by the doctor and controlled by him. This may necessitate two or three good, watertight plastic, bakelite or fibreglass compartmentalized packing cases. There may also be individual medical kits designed for each member and issued to cover periods when the doctor cannot possibly be present.)

VEHICLES

Winch
Tow chain
Fuel
Spare fuel cans
Spot lamps
Greases
Oil
Tool kit
Spare parts
For a comprehensive list of recommended tools and vehicle equipment see *A Guide to Land-Rover Expeditions* (Rover Co. Ltd., Solihull), also diagram on page 245.

COMMUNICATIONS EQUIPMENT

Radios HF
Radios VHF
Receiver (for World News and meteorological forecasts)
Portable generators (e.g. *Honda*)
Power and battery connectors and leads
Antenna equipment including feeders, insulators, pulleys and guys, plus spares
Tape recorder
Dictaphone
Batteries for all equipment (ideally *Mallory* Cells)
Mini Flares
Sarbe Beacons

SOME POINTERS

Certain points arise from these lists which I suggest are worth noting and emphasizing:

1. Items which are perhaps most useful of all and never in sufficient quantity are masking tape, assorted sizes of plastic bags, assorted plastic containers for kitchen use, packing rope, felt-tipped pens and magic markers.
2. Much freight weight can be cut by ascertaining the availability of local purchase items. For example, all cooking pots and pans can usually be bought locally.
3. Similarly, the amount of pre-packed food taken (and this can account for half the payload) is directly related to the availability and price of local fresh rations.

4. When scientists are involved, do not underestimate the bulk and weight of equipment that they are likely to want to bring along. No doubt all of this is essential for their task, but it is often heavy and large.
5. Do not forget items for recreation. Often an expedition can be stormed in or have to wait a long time for transport. Books, Scrabble, liar dice, playing cards and a volley ball—for example—are worth the effort of taking.
6. It is always worth visiting a good expedition equipment shop like Black and Edgington or Pindisports in London to see the range of equipment available today and to pick up tips for equipment planning.

PACKAGING

The packing of expedition equipment and provision of cases can be very expensive. It is a specialist subject but there is no doubt that good plywood or plastic type boxes are worth the cost. With food packs, perhaps banded cardboard, with waterproofing paper, is acceptable but anything less is not likely to stand up to the conditions of movement, weather, crows and rodents.

In mountaineering expeditions it is usual to have a good, lockable, personal box. For other equipment sensible size boxes in wood can be used later for kitchen and office building, shelving, firewood and repacking.

Most important in packaging is to bear in mind the weight factor. Ideally, smaller packs want to be made up into larger manpackable loads.

PERSONAL

On the personal clothing side, plenty of spare socks and good fitting footwear are essential. It is also true that two or three lightweight sweaters are more effective and more flexible than one very heavy one. For cold weather, silk gloves with finger mittens and *Dacksteing* mits are recommended. For external garments such as anoraks and wind suits, it is wise to select a zip that does not freeze up or tear the cold skin. Whenever possible the use of *velcro* is highly recommended.

I have not mentioned arms, ammunition or explosives but these are sometimes taken when appropriate clearances can be given and the nature of the expedition requires their use. In most cases a shotgun and a .22 rifle are more than enough. Do not forget the cleaning kits.

FOOD PACKS

The actual composition of the food packs is a matter for the Food Member. Good examples of menus can be found in the appendixes of the recent large-scale expedition books and of course these vary according to climate, geography and duration of the expedition. There are, however, a few salient points mainly connected with the weight usage factor. For example, dehydrated foods are very good because they are light, but they are only of use if and when there is a plentiful supply of easily obtainable, pure water. High up on mountains and in the Arctic or desert regions little water is available. Even if snow and ice can be melted, this uses more fuel and tends to negate the weight-saving factor.

Perhaps the most important thing in choosing food is to get products or combinations that people like and will actually eat. In other words, flavour is very important. It is no use taking a well-composed calorie ration which remains largely uneaten.

Another point to remember is that local helpers on an expedition will certainly want and expect to be catered for to some extent. I have found that because of this and the fact that small split-up groups are less economical to cater for, the consumption of rations is often about 40% more than catered for.

In calculating the actual numbers and quantities of rations it is best to work on a man/day basis. According to the size of groups, rations may be packed into 12 man/day, 10 man/day, 5 man/day or 2 man/day packs. These packs can either be completely self-contained or they can be composed of something like 750 grammes per man per day packed allowing for a local supplement of another 750 grammes per man per day thus making a ration of 1.5 kilogrammes per man/day. For assault rations in, say, a 2 man/day pack the answer might be a self-contained 2.5 kilogramme box, giving 1.25 kilogrammes per man/day with no local supplement. In areas like a Base Camp or close to civilization it might be as little as 500 grammes per man/day relying on plenty of local produce to make up the bulk. There is no end to the permutations but due consideration should be given to the overall weight and associated cost of packing and freight.

Whatever the end result it is advisable that ration packs contain matches, paper tissues or towels, toilet paper, candle and tin opener. Over and above this there should be specially composed kitchen boxes which can include cleaning materials and bulk supplies of things like sugar, tea, coffee, liquor, cigarettes, flour, rice, vegetables, plastic cans, cookers and so on. From this supply can be made up camp kits which should have everything in them necessary to set up and maintain a camp.

Another well used and worthwhile idea is the 'goodie bag'. This is a bag or container made up of luxuries which can be sent up a mountain to the camps or air dropped or supplied to parties in the jungle or expedition area. They are very popular and can be a valuable aid to morale but someone has to think about it and prepare it in advance.

Nowadays there are several commercial food packs on the market and some of these, obtainable from climbing and expedition shops, are very good. In addition, Horlicks do a useful pack, Batchelors do catering packs and the firm of Andrew Lusk Ltd, 4 Thames Road, Barking, Essex (Tel 01 594 3822) specialize in the acquisition and packing of expedition rations. The result is expensive but they are excellent and will make up menus to your choosing. Finally, there is the Army or Compo pack which of course is still about the best but not always available for civilian expeditions and rather heavy for normal use.

TESTING OF KIT

There is no substitute for pre-packing testing. Nothing is more infuriating on an expedition than to arrive on location, unpack and then find that a vital piece of clothing or equipment does not fit or does not work. Time spent in testing beforehand is never wasted.

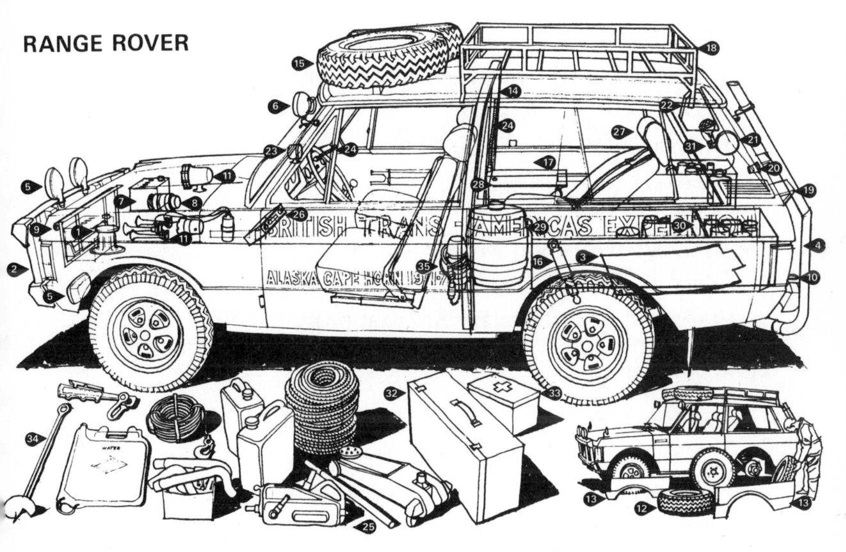

1 Front mounted capstan winch 3,000 lb capacity
2 Reinforced bumper/cow catcher guard
3 Petrol tank undershield
4 Raised exhaust extension
5 Four Quartz-Iodine spot and fog lights
6 Two swivel spot lights
7 Split charge two battery system
8 Heavy duty alternator
9 Radiator muff
10 Four extra towing eyes
11 Sirens and air horns
12 Swamp tyres
13 Removable wing panels
14 Roll-bar
15 Roof mounted spare wheels
16 Special low-temperature shock absorbers
17 Insulated body panels
18 Roof rack
19 Steps on tailgate
20 Power point in rear of vehicle for cooker etc.
21 Heated rear screen
22 Wiper/washer equipment for rear screen
23 Extra instruments – tachometer, oil pressure and temperature gauges, ammeter for split charge system
24 Map reading and interior lights
25 Tirfor jack
26 Stereo-tape player and radio
27 Reclining seat with full safety harness and headrest
28 Built-in safe
29 Water keg
30 Partitioned stowage lockers
31 Inspection light, 26ft lead
32 Fully comprehensive tool kit
33 Medical supplies
34 Extra equipment, hand winches, ground anchors, cable, tow ropes etc
35 Coffee maker

BIBLIOGRAPHY

EXPEDITION PLANNING

The Expedition Organiser's Guide by John Blashford-Snell and Richard Snailham (Scientific Exploration Society and *The Daily Telegraph*, 1971)

Handbook for Expeditions (Brathay Exploration Group and *The Geographical Magazine*, 1971)

Hints to Travellers—two volumes (The Royal Geographical Society and John Murray, 1938)

Off The Beaten Track: An Expedition and Travel Handbook (World Expeditionary Association)

FUND RAISING

Directory of Grant-Making Trusts (Charities Aid Fund of the National Council of Social Service, 1974)

Educational Charities (National Union of Students, 1974)

EQUIPMENT

Field Studies—A Guide to Equipment for Field Studies (Griffin and George)

Guide to Land-Rover Expeditions (Rover Co. Ltd., Solihull)

PHOTOGRAPHY

All About Photographing Animals and Birds by David Hodgson (Pelham Books, 1974)

Wildlife Photography: A Field Guide by Eric Hosking and John Gooders (Hutchinson, 1973)

Photography on Expeditions by D. H. O. John (Focal Press, 1965)
Travel Photography (Time Life Books, 1973)
What You Must Know when You Travel with a Camera (Harian Publications, New York)

HEALTH AND MEDICINE

Traveller's Guide to Health by Lt Col James M. Adam RAMC (Royal Geographical Society and Hodder and Stoughton, 1961)
Exploration Medicine edited by Edholm and Bacharach (John Wright & Sons, 1965)
Medical Care for Mountain Climbers by Dr Peter Steele (Heinemann, 1976)
The Traveller's Health Guide by Dr A. Turner (Tom Stacey, 1971)
Mountain Medicine by Michael Ward (Crosby Lockwood, 1975)
Preservation of Personal Health in Warm Climates (The Ross Institute of Tropical Medicine, 1971)

DESERT EXPLORATION

Journeys in the Libyan Desert 1929 and 1930 by R. A. Bagnold (*Geographical Journal* 78, 6:526–30)
A Simple Method of Navigation in Deserts by D. N. Hall (*Geographical Journal* 133, 2:192–205)
Further Notes of Navigation in Deserts by D. N. Hall (*Geographical Journal* 133, 4:508–11)
Desert Navigation by T. H. Sheppard (*Geographical Journal* 136, 2:235–39)
The Sahara is Yours (A Handbook for Desert Travellers) by Jon Stevens (Constable, 1969)
Arabian Sands by Wilfred Thesiger (Longmans, 1959)
War-Time Exploration with the Sudan Defence Force in the Libyan Desert by J. W. Wright (*Geographical Journal* 105, 3 & 4; 100–1)

THE POLAR REGIONS

Arctic Animals by F. Bruemmer (McGraw-Hill Ryerson, Toronto, 1972)

The Crossing of Antarctica by V. Fuchs and E. Hillary (Cassell, 1958)

The Reindeer People by Marie Herbert (Hodder and Stoughton, 1976)

The Snow People by Marie Herbert (Barrie and Jenkins, 1973)

Across the Top of the World by Wally Herbert (Longmans, 1969)

Eskimos by Wally Herbert (Collins, 1976)

Polar Deserts by Wally Herbert (Collins, 1971)

A World of Men by Wally Herbert (Eyre and Spottiswoode, 1968)

Arctic Survival Guide by A. Innes-Taylor (S.A.S. Stockholm, 1967)

The Antarctic by H. King (Blandford Press, 1969)

The Arctic Frontier edited by R. St. J. Macdonald (University of Toronto Press, 1966)

A History of Polar Exploration by D. Mountfield (Hamlyn, 1974)

Hunters of the Northern Ice by Richard Nelson (University of Chicago Press, London, 1969)

Polar Research—A Survey (National Science Foundation Washington, DC, 1970)

Animals of the Antarctic: Ecology of the Far South by Bernard Stonehouse (P. Lowe, 1972)

MOUNTAINS

Mountaineering by D. T. Roscoe (Faber and Faber, 1976)

EXPEDITIONS

In the Steps of Stanley by John Blashford-Snell (Hutchinson, 1975)

Where the Trails Run Out by John Blashford-Snell (Hutchinson, 1974)
A Fighting Chance by Chay Blyth and John Ridgway (Hamlyn, 1966)
The Impossible Voyage by Chay Blyth (Hodder and Stoughton, 1971)
Theirs is the Glory by Chay Blyth (Hodder and Stoughton, 1974)
Annapurna South Face by Chris Bonington (Cassell, 1971)
Changabang by Chris Bonington and others (Heinemann, 1975)
Everest South West Face by Chris Bonington (Hodder and Stoughton, 1973)
Everest the Hard Way by Chris Bonington (Hodder and Stoughton, 1976)
The Hundred Days of Darien by Russell Braddon (Collins, 1974)
Exploration Fawcett by Lt Col P. M. Fawcett (Hutchinson, 1953)
The Headless Valley by Captain Sir Ranulph Fiennes (Hodder and Stoughton, 1973)
Ice Fall in Norway by Captain Sir Ranulph Fiennes (Hodder and Stoughton, 1972)
A Talent for Trouble by Captain Sir Ranulph Fiennes (Hodder and Stoughton, 1970)
A Pattern of Peoples by Robin Hanbury-Tenison (Angus and Robinson, 1975)
A Question of Survival by Robin Hanbury-Tenison (Angus and Robinson, 1973)
The Rough and the Smooth by Robin Hanbury-Tenison (Robert Hale, 1969)
The Eiger by Dougal Haston (Cassell, 1974)
In High Places by Dougal Haston (Cassell, 1972)
Fatu Hiva by Thor Heyerdahl (George Allen and Unwin, 1974)
Kon-Tiki by Thor Heyerdahl (George Allen and Unwin, 1950)
The Ra Expeditions by Thor Heyerdahl (George Allen and Unwin, 1971)
Ghar Parau by David Judson (Cassell, 1973)

A World of My Own by Robin Knox-Johnston (Cassell, 1969)
Climb to the Lost World by Hamish McInnes (Hodder and Stoughton, 1974)
The Voyage of Geneve by Michel Mermod (John Murray, 1973)
A Short Walk in the Hindu Kush by Eric Newby (Hodder and Stoughton, 1958 and 1972)
World Atlas of Exploration by Eric Newby (Mitchell Beazley, 1975)
Amazon Journey: From the Source to the Sea by John Ridgway (Hodder and Stoughton, 1972)
Cockleshell Journey by John Ridgway (Hodder and Stoughton, 1974)
Storm Passage by John Ridgway (Hodder and Stoughton, 1975)
A Fighting Chance by John Ridgway and Chay Blyth (Hamlyn)
The Blue Nile Revealed by Richard Snailham (Chatto & Windus, 1970)
A Giant Among Rivers by Richard Snailham (Hutchinson, 1976)
My Amazon Adventure by Sebastian Snow (Odhams, 1956)
Half a Dozen of the Other by Sebastian Snow (Hodder and Stoughton, 1972)
The Rucksack Man by Sebastian Snow (Hodder and Stoughton, 1976)
Doctor on Everest by Peter Steele (Hodder and Stoughton, 1972)
Two and Two Halves to Bhutan by Peter Steele (Hodder and Stoughton, 1970)
The Marsh Arabs by Wilfred Thesiger (Longmans, 1964)
Ice with Everything by H. W. Tilman (Nautical Publishing Company)
Cucumber Sandwiches in the Andes by John Ure (Constable, 1973)
In This Short Span: Himalayan Mountaineering and Exploration by Michael Ward (Gollancz, 1972)

Expedition reports

British Trans-Americas Expedition Report (Scientific Exploration Society)

Great Abbai (Blue Nile) Expedition Report (Scientific Exploration Society)

The Zaïre River Expedition Report (Scientific Exploration Society)

The Royal Geographical Society Library contains expedition reports going back many years and covering all parts of the world.

Further information and advice can be obtained from:

The Scientific Exploration Society Ltd.,
Home Farm,
Mildenhall,
Marlborough,
Wiltshire

The World Expeditionary Association,
45 Brompton Road,
Knightsbridge,
London SW3 1DE

BIOGRAPHICAL NOTES

ALISTAIR BALLANTINE

Born in 1948, brought up in England. Read Geography at Cambridge and became interested in expeditions. While at university he joined expeditions to Europe and to North Africa. After leaving Cambridge and working three years in business, he joined WEXAS as Chairman in 1974. He is now deeply involved in helping advise and promote expeditions leaving the UK.

Lt Col JOHN BLASHFORD-SNELL, MBE, Royal Engineers

Born in 1936, married with two daughters. He has seen active service in Cyprus, Oman and Ulster. As an instructor at Sandhurst with special responsibility for organizing Adventure Training, he launched sixty expeditions to all parts of the world. Since 1958 he has been the leader or member of eighteen expeditions, including the Great Abbai Expedition in 1968, which made the first descent and exploration of the Blue Nile; the British Trans-Americas Expedition which involved making the first complete vehicle crossing of the notorious Darien Gap; and the Zaïre River Expedition which he led in 1974–5. He has received numerous awards including the MBE in 1969, the Livingstone Medal of the Royal Scottish Geographical Society in 1975 and Segrave Trophy, also in 1975. At present he is commander of the Royal Engineers Junior Leaders Regiment at Dover, and Chairman of the Scientific Exploration Society.

CHAY BLYTH CBE

Born in 1940, joined the Parachute Regiment at the age of eighteen, and served in a number of overseas postings. In 1966, he rowed the Atlantic with John Ridgway, and for his part in the exploit was awarded the British Empire Medal. Chay Blyth left the Army in 1967, and in 1968 sailed non-stop single-handed to South Africa in the *Sunday Times* Round the World Race. In 1970–1, he achieved the first non-stop, single-handed sail round the world against the wind and prevailing currents from east to west, for which he was awarded the CBE, and a year later with his crew, was the first to cross the line in the Whitbread Round the World Race. He currently organizes sailing cruises.

Major ROGER CHAPMAN, MBE, Green Howards
Roger Chapman's first interest in white water came when he was a canoe instructor at an Outward Bound School in Norway. In 1968 on the Great Abbai expedition, he led the white water team that successfully tackled the hitherto unnavigated upper reaches of the Blue Nile in three small Avon *Redshanks—Faith, Hope* and *Charity*. Since this trip, he has been involved with seven more expeditions in Norway, Central and South America. He also led the white water team on the Zaïre River Expedition, but was temporarily suspended from expeditioning after he got amoebic abscesses on the liver and had the unenviable experience of being operated on by a gynaecologist on the banks of the river. Between expeditions he has been on active service several times in Northern Ireland as a Regular Army Officer in the Green Howards; and has produced a documentary for Independent Television on a remote religious sect in South America.

RUSSELL GURNEE
An explorer, speleologist, author and industrialist. Leader of numerous expeditions to explore and study caves in Central America, South America and the Caribbean. Past President and recipient of Honorary Life Membership in the National Speleological Society and the Explorers Club. Made original surveys of the Rio Camuy Cave in Puerto Rico; designed equipment used in the exploration of caves. United States

representative to International Speleological Congresses in Italy, Germany, Yugoslavia, Czechoslovakia and Cuba.

Lt Col DAVID HALL, Royal Engineers

Born in London in 1933, married with three daughters. Educated at the London Choir School, and at Carlisle and Gregsons (Jimmys), joined the Royal Engineers in 1952 and served in Korea. He has led a number of expeditions and travelled on camel in the Libyan Desert and the Southern Sahara. The last expedition, an international study in Niger, earned him the Royal Geographical Society's Mrs Patrick Ness Award. He has written a number of papers on navigation for the *Geographical Journal*; and a paper on the problems of acclimatization to hot, dry climates which earned him the Helbron Prize of the Royal Military College of Science. He is Honorary Foreign Secretary of the Royal Geographical Society and a Founder Member of the Society for Libyan Studies.

WALLY HERBERT

Born in 1934, he went on his first Antarctic expedition in 1955 at the age of twenty-one, and up to now has spent a total of over ten years in the field and dog-sledged well over 17,000 miles (27,400 kilometres) across some of the roughest routes in the polar regions. His sledging journeys during the four years he spent in the Antarctic resulted in maps covering over 45,000 square miles (116,500 square kilometres) of previously unexplored country, and the only descent since Amundsen of the Norwegian route to the Pole. In the Arctic in 1966–7 he also retraced the route of Dr Frederick Cook and in 1968, after four years of planning and training, he set out from Alaska with three companions and four teams of dogs on a 16-month journey of almost 6,000 kilometres across the Arctic Ocean to Spitsbergen via the Pole of Inaccessibility and the North Pole, since when he has spent a further two years hunting and travelling with the Polar Eskimos in preparation for a journey of 12,000 kilometres by dog sledge and sealskin boat. He is the recipient of a Polar Medal and bar, the

Livingstone Gold Medal of the Royal Scottish Geographical Society and the Founders Gold Medal of the Royal Geographical Society for his 'outstanding contribution to polar exploration and survey'.

Major KELVIN KENT, late Royal Signals
Born in 1939, is best known as one of the world's most experienced expedition administrators. He served with the Gurkha Signal Regiment and has been on many mountaineering expeditions in the Himalayas. He suffered severe frostbite to his fingers whilst on the 1972 Everest South West Face Expedition when, in the face of the most appalling conditions, he continued to carry loads up to 24,600 feet—without oxygen. He is equally at home in the jungle and was deputy leader of the British Trans-Americas Expedition that made the first complete crossing of the infamous Darien Gap in 1972. John Blashford-Snell (the Leader) later said that the success of that expedition was largely due to the logistic planning and tenacity of Kelvin Kent and his administrative team.

He has now retired from the British Army and lives with his American wife, Jennie, and their two children in Montrose, Colorado.

Dr CHRISTOPHER ROADS
Born in 1934, has a degree in history and a PhD in military history from Cambridge. He went on his first underwater expedition to Egypt in 1952 and was involved with a series of marine archaeological expeditions between 1955–66. In 1967 he set up the Cambridge Coral Research Group which has been operating in the Red Sea for the last eight years. He is Deputy Director of the Imperial War Museum.

Dr MALCOLM SLESSER
Has been climbing mountains for forty years. He went on his first expedition to Greenland in 1950, and spent a year there in the far north two years later. He organized and led his first expedition to the Staunings Alps of East Greenland in 1958, and

subsequently led expeditions to the Andes, Yukon, and took over the leadership of the British Soviet Pamirs Expedition to the Peak of Communism in 1962. He is a member of the Scottish Mountaineering Club and Club Alpin Français and has climbed twenty-one virgin peaks. He lives in Perthshire with his wife and two children.

Dr PETER STEELE MB, FRCS (Ed)
Born 1935. Started climbing at an Outward Bound School, later becoming an instructor. Two mountain exploration expeditions in North Africa. Qualified as a doctor in 1960 and went to work for the Grenfell Association in Newfoundland. Climbed Popocatepetl in Mexico. Worked in a mission hospital in Kathmandu, Nepal, with his wife and together they climbed and explored an unmapped area of West Nepal. In 1964 took charge of the Grenfell Flying Doctor service in Northern Labrador. In 1967, with his wife and two children, both under the age of four, spent five months on muleback and foot crossing the Himalayan kingdom of Bhutan. Returned to East Nepal and Sikkim in 1969. Physician to the International Everest Expedition in 1971. In 1972 he travelled round South America with his ten-year-old son and climbed in the Cordillera Vilcabamba. He is at present in practice in Whitehorse, Yukon Territory, Canada.